NO RAIN IN THOSE CLOUDS

Link House

NO RAIN IN THOSE CLOUDS

Being an Account of my Father John Smith's Life and Farming from 1862 to the Present Day

By

DAVID SMITH

DRAWINGS BY

J. K. POPHAM

LONDON
J. M. DENT AND SONS LIMITED

All rights reserved
Made in Great Britain
at The Temple Press Letchworth
for
J. M. Dent & Sons Ltd.
Aldine House Bedford St. London
First published 1943

Some extracts from this book have already appeared in *The Countryman* and are reprinted here with the kind permission of its editor.

D. S.

FOREWORD

'I wish to God,' said the foreman, 'that I had a memory half as good as yours.'

He was discussing with my father some technical point concerning field dressing, and father had just quoted what he had done for the same thing some fifty years before.

Father only grinned, and two or three of the men who were standing round listening laughed. Father's memory is proverbial, almost a legend, and we, who work with him, are proud of it. In fact, we 're inclined to boast about it to strangers.

He is always in his best vein after a good supper on a Saturday night, particularly if someone he likes happens to be having supper with us. I defy any one to recover in print his inimitable style as a raconteur, and although I had often considered setting down some of his stories in writing, it took the foreman's emphatic phrase to make up my mind for me.

Here then I shall hope to set down some account of my father's life and work, of the men with whom he worked and of the land he worked, and still works, on.

TO
MY FATHER AND MOTHER

CONTENTS

ILLUSTRATIONS

J.K.Popham

CHAPTER I

LINK HOUSE

IT was the beautiful magnolia in the front of the house that gave it an air. You noticed it first as you drove up the yard past the corn barn and the pond, and all your impressions of the house were afterwards somehow entangled with it, so that the house, which was really ugly, always seemed a cut above ordinary farmhouses.

The farm lies in the small parish of West Hanningfield, six miles south-south-east of Chelmsford. To the east and south are two more parishes of the same name, the whole district being called Haningfelda in Domesday Book. It is heavy clay soil, which, farmed well by men who know it, produces good crops. The district has as varied a history as any English land. The Rev. Philip Morant, in his *Antiquities of Essex*, 1768, notes that 'before the Conquest these lands were holden by one Friebert, one Norman, Oin a Dane and three other Freemen.' After the Conquest Odo, Bishop of Baycux, and William of Warenne, familiar names, added these villages to their handsome share of the spoil. The easiest way to describe West Hanningfield's locality is to say the village lies roughly half-way between the Chelmsford–Southend and Chelmsford–Billericay roads.

Link House stands on the east side of the village, some

four fields from the Southend road, and the house itself is one meadow back from the road to the village, with barns and yards on both sides, but with a clear space in front of it, looking across the meadow and the road, and over the Sandon brook valley to distant fields and woods beyond. No one, however, could really describe the house as having a view. There are few farmhouses with views in Essex.

The building itself is an old plaster house at the back with a bit built on in front of brick, consisting of two upstair and two downstair rooms. To the right of the house were the stables, cow shed and bullock yards, and a large barn, behind which again was the stack yard, and on the left another barn with a bullock yard, and immediately beside the house a large pond. It was this pond which caused one of my father's few lapses from grace which he has never been able to explain satisfactorily. It appears, from scanty evidence, that he was directly responsible for the death by drowning of a large family of ducklings, though exactly how or why this happened it is impossible to say, because all the other witnesses of the disaster are long since dead, and father, who was five at the time, won't talk!

Behind the house stretches a garden of something over an acre, together with the orchard. It was in this orchard that the poplars grew, standing out clear, a landmark for miles in the surrounding countryside. People who came on a visit, and who could not be met at Chelmsford station, were advised to 'tell your cab-driver to drive along the Southend road for about six miles, till he sees our poplars on his right, and then take the first turning on the right.' This was always far safer than saying: 'Link House, West Hanningfield.'

A stream runs through the orchard, and used to be full of watercress, which visitors occasionally picked and brought in proudly, when they had to be tactfully told that the stream had some connection with the cesspool. In the spring and early summer the cow-parsley grew there to a tremendous height, and looked lovely. It was a very fertile orchard.

There were tremendous outhouses at the back of the old house. First the scullery, then the brew house and kitchen, and lastly the tub house, so called because the tubs of beer were left to cool there. All these outhouses had tiled floors, and had to be scrubbed. It was bad luck on the maids if brewing and pig killing came due together.

The kitchen opened into a passage which connected the two parts of the house. Opposite was the breakfast-room, a small dark-brown room, which looked out over a croquet lawn to the pond. This had been enlarged in my grandfather's time, as his family grew. Previously it was just a large cupboard where the wine was kept, and somehow it never quite lost the character of an old-fashioned cupboard. The farm books were kept here in a high desk, and it was the place where cattle dealers and neighbouring farmers were brought in to clinch a deal and have a drink. There was never a farmer yet who clinched a deal in a drawing-room.

At the bottom of the passage a door on the right led down some steep stone steps to the cellar. It was always beautifully cool, and kept the beer and butter in wonderful condition. In my grandfather's time there were two casks that held eight hogsheads and two casks that held five. When my father was young he was put inside the casks to limewash them before they were filled with beer. Before father was put in they tried the air with a candle; if the candle continued to burn brightly it was: 'All right, boy; in with you, and mind you scrape 'em well first!' Sometimes in the winter when the pond rose from the rains, the cellar flooded suddenly, and people who went down without a light for a quick pint at supper-time got their feet wet.

Upstairs, apart from the two best bedrooms in the front of the house, there were four bedrooms on the same floor and two big attics above. Besides these, there was a curious middle room, which joined the two parts of the house together. It had no windows, and a door at each end, and was treated more or less as a landing. It was here that my grandmother, who was terrified of thunder, used to gather her family about her during a heavy storm, and pray for deliverance. Before entering what she regarded as her thunder-proof shelter she would be careful to pull most of the blinds, and to cover up all the looking-glasses in the house; then there was nothing to do but watch and pray.

As my grandfather's family increased the elder ones were put up in the attics, which were turned superficially into bedrooms. My father, who was the eldest son, and a brother, had one each. The house had a slate roof, which meant that the rooms were extremely hot in summer, and that in the winter the boys had to break the ice on the water jugs. This lasted till my grandfather died, and then my father was given a bedroom just over the kitchen, with the head of his bed immediately over the house bells. This enabled my grandmother to wake him early in the event of a thunderstorm or any other major disaster.

In 1848 or thereabouts Link House was known as Union Farm. Exactly when or why 'Union' became 'Link' has never been known. Possibly because other farms became 'linked' with it, and were all worked as the one farm, though even so 'Union' would have remained a good name. There were three other farms which were worked with the Link House land: Partridge's, three fields away, in front of the farmhouse down in the valley of the Sandon brook; Cannon Barns, away to the east, over a slight sloping brow of land; and Wyatts, half way between Link House and the Southend road; the whole comprising about 625 acres. Partridge's was on the site of an old manor, officially known as Parages, which was granted by Henry VIII in 1541 to one John

Cannon, citizen and merchant taylor of London. It seems probable that this wealthy gentleman or his heirs were responsible for the building of, or had some connection with, Cannon Barns. A Richard Cannon, dying in 1605, left for the poor of West Hanningfield and the neighbouring parish of Rettendon a cottage, barn, and nineteen acres of land at Hockley, near Southend.

On Sundays grandfather would lead his family across the horse meadow, and up the road to church. Father remembers that in the spring, when his sisters all had new clothes to wear to go to church, they all hoped the birds would christen them as they passed under the old elms. The ensuing good luck for the year would more than counter any possible damage done to their clothes.

The church stands on the right-hand side of the road, about four hundred yards from Link House. It is an ancient structure, with a wooden tower and spire, and a peal of five bells. When father was born they were rung by some old villagers to celebrate the arrival of yet another John Smith into the world. From here the road winds away to the left and uphill, past a few cottages snuggling round the 'Ivy House,' well described by its name, past the smithy and the large square rectory standing back from the road, and past the small village school. Then at the top of the hill you pass another inn, the 'Compasses,' another small group of houses, and the old bakery. To the left the road forks away to South Hanningfield and Stock, and to the right to further outlying cottages, and so on to the Galleywood road, or by back roads to Baddow. When the last outlying cottages are past and the Galleywood road is only one hundred yards away, any one who stops and turns about may see that rare phenomenon in Essex, a real long-distance view. In front the land slopes away over the Hanningfields into blue distance, and to the right, it seems, almost to the Thames estuary and the Kent hills.

In 1911, during the extreme heat wave of that year, Link
House must have shown up well from this vantage point,
for my father had the slate roof whitewashed. It made no
difference at all to the heat of the bedrooms, but created a
good deal of local interest. The year 1911 went down as
that which was 'so wonderful hot John Smith were took
queer and had his roof whitewashed.'

CHAPTER II

GRANDPARENTS

'Oh, yes, he liked his beer,' they said.

The one thing the old labourers remembered about my great-grandfather, Edward Smith, was how he used to sit on the front doorstep of Link House at five o'clock in the morning during harvest time and eat his breakfast. This consisted of a quart mug of beer and a plate of cold salt pork.

He seems to have worked hard, and enjoyed himself. He was responsible for either chalking or liming some five hundred and sixty acres of land in West Hanningfield, and used to get up along with his men at five in the morning and drive a cart himself six miles to a neighbouring village station to fetch his material. His chalked land was a great heritage for his descendants; and though this land has lain derelict for twenty years, it is now at last being brought back into cultivation, and should yield good crops.

Great-grandfather had no use for a man who couldn't drink his bottle of port after dinner over a game of three-card loo. This probably accounts for the story that he was 'a wonder to cuff the boys over the head fust thing in the mornin'.'

He had only two sons: my grandfather, and another who

died when a young man. He was very pleased when my grandfather married in 1859, and he took great delight in leaving his son at home to work the farm and taking his daughter-in-law out for the day. One event which gave him an excuse for this was Galleywood Races, which were held annually at the beginning of August on Galleywood Common, about four miles away from Link House. The races were a great local occasion then, a two-day meeting being held, the first day mainly patronized by the gentry, and the second by the farm-workers and local townspeople of Chelmsford. The Galleywood course has three claims to fame. It was patronized by King Charles II, it is said to be the only course in England which makes a complete circle round the village church, and it has a killing uphill finish. William White, in his *History of Essex*, 1848, notes that 'the races are well attended, rarely wanting either genteel company or plenty of good horses.' All the Link House roadside hedges were trimmed and any patches of nettles or thistles in the front meadow were scythed a day or so before the neighbours and gentry passed that way to the meeting.

Great-grandfather, who took great pride in a spanking horse and gig, drove off in fine style that August morning, with his daughter-in-law beside him. From all accounts the pair seem to have had a most successful day. The right horses won, good friends were there in plenty, and the champagne flowed. At all events grandmother confided to her husband that she was glad to be home. It had been a most enjoyable day, she said, but the journey back had been a little trying. Great-grandfather had driven home at great speed, rounding corners on one wheel, and passing everything on the road.

There were not many further occasions for such enjoyable outings, for great-grandfather died in the following February, a month before his first grandchild was born. A week or so before his death he had been talking to old George Snell, who was brewing in the tub house.

'Make it a good brew, George,' he said, 'ready for the boy!'

He might have been a little disappointed when a month later my father's eldest sister, Sophie, was born, and it was two years later, in 1862, that my father, the boy who was to appreciate the brew, was born.

Grandfather seems to have followed on at Link House in much the same tradition, except that he had a much larger family. My grandmother, who came from Devonshire, was an extremely capable and handsome woman, with a genius for getting things done, but having other people do the work. However, she did do a great deal herself, and with a family of eight children in a large and rambling farmhouse she certainly needed some help. The two girls who came first, Sophie and Kate, were born within the year, then my father, John Edward, in 1862; then twins, Annie and Frank, followed by two more girls, Lilian and Alice, and another son, Ted. This must have been the peak period of busy-ness and industry at Link House, and during this time three pigs a year were killed for the house —one at Michaelmas, another at Christmas, and the third at Easter.

My grandparents were complete opposites in character, grandfather being an extremely generous and kindly man, while grandmother, though not mean, could hardly be described as over-imbued with the milk of human kindness and sympathy. Probably she felt that her own family was enough for any one woman to look after. Grandfather once supplied a poor family in the village with bread for a whole winter, but only with the strict injunction that his wife was on no account to hear of it.

For many years grandfather was a churchwarden at the village church, which, in those days, had a musicians' gallery. Grandfather must have had a busy time during the services, which he attended morning and evening, for, besides his duties as warden, he also played the flute in the choir. The musicians' gallery was high up at the back of the church, with the dimness of the belfry behind, and my father was sometimes allowed to sit up there during the service as a special treat. His children often tried to induce grandfather to play his flute to them in the winter evenings at Link House, but it was only rarely that they succeeded. Then he would sit in front of the fire in the little breakfast-room, with the children clustered round him, and play away to their hearts' content till bedtime. In the end it was grandfather himself who ended the days of the musicians' gallery. He opened a fund in the village for a church organ, which was installed soon afterwards. His flute was put away into the old china cabinet, where it remains, dusty and broken now, to this day.

At regular intervals grandmother, who was in charge of the poultry on the farms, made a tour of inspection. This was not looked forward to by the woman responsible for the poultry at each farm. Grandmother on the warpath is still spoken of in hushed voices by any who saw her. She wore a long and very full skirt, which she lifted up off the ground with her right hand, and when she was in a temper she moved it rapidly backwards and forwards with a sort of whipping movement. This seems to be the characteristic picture of my grandmother which every one who knew her remembers. It was just the same during the spring-cleaning when father and some of the men were beating the carpets in the front meadow. She was always behind them, hurrying them up, a compact, well-built figure, skirt whipping back and forth as she tartly chided any loiterer.

There was one incident in which grandmother figured that few who saw it ever forgot. It was a harvest festival service, and the decorators had been more than usually thorough. Even the swinging oil lamps which hang over the aisle had their small sheaves of corn and evergreen draped round their brass frames. Grandmother came sweeping into church as usual, her head held high and upon it a tall decorated bonnet. On she went, up the aisle towards her pew near the front of the church. The congregation watched, fascinated, as first one and then another of the lamps was narrowly missed. The third and last lamp before her pew proved her undoing; bonnet and decorations met and held! There was a brief moment of stress and strain and then the decoration gave, and grandmother continued to her pew, with her bonnet freshly trimmed. To the delight and admiration of the congregation she sat out the service and made her exit without acknowledging in any way that she was aware of anything unusual.

My grandfather's chief worry was his landlord, whom he found it very difficult to get on with; but he used to forget his worries when he went shooting. He was an excellent shot, save on one occasion when my father was present. Grandfather and two men were ferreting the banks of a field called Gomer's Eight Acres, and though the rabbits were bolting well and fast, he was completely unable to hit them, and missed one after another. Eventually he called a halt, and shouted to one of the men, Joe May, who was the landlord of a pub in the village called the 'Ivy House,' and only worked part of his time for us.

'Joe,' shouted grandfather, 'go up to the "Ivy House" and bring back half a gallon of old beer and some biscuits.'

Joe went off, and grandfather sat down to wait. When the beer arrived he drank three glasses straight off, and then the men put the ferrets in again.

He never missed another rabbit all day. He said he couldn't help hitting them—they looked as big as sheep. Beer was beer then.

Edward Badeley, the landlord, and his brother Henry

sometimes spent long week-ends at Link House for the shooting. Arriving on Thursday they would stay until the following Tuesday. On Friday, Saturday, and Monday they would be shooting, and on Sunday they would set off, often with father as guide, to visit one of the neighbouring churches. Henry Badeley had a great sense of humour, and often father was hard put to it to keep a straight face as a small fat parson would suddenly be named, *sotto voce*, 'Roger Tichborne,' or an excellent imitation of some pompous sexton's sonorous 'a-men' sounded by his side throughout the service.

These visits kept grandmother very busy. Extra help would be summoned in from the farms, and the kitchen and outhouses would be full of small children getting in the way and women busy with the cooking. These many cooks did, on one occasion, spoil the broth. A rabbit pie, for which the rabbits had been very thoroughly hung, was prepared, but no ventilator was placed in the centre for the cooking gases to escape. The pie was much enjoyed at supper, but the sleepers at Link House spent a disturbed night. Father, waking in the night, said the house seemed alive. At breakfast next morning Mr. Badeley shook his fist at grandmother, but no word was said.

Grandfather and grandmother ruled their children with the traditional iron hand within the velvet glove. Grandmother, who was something of a gourmet, used to provide her family with a huge joint on Sundays, but always had some delicacies for herself. These were tacitly ignored by the children; a suggestion from one of them that they would like a small piece of mother's chicken might, they felt, be badly received.

Father once contradicted my grandfather over some point one Sunday morning when grandfather was cutting asparagus in the kitchen garden. Grandfather straightened his back slowly and stood up, and the next thing father remembers is picking himself up out of the hedge and walking quietly away. He mostly agreed with grandfather after that, and got on very well with him.

Grandfather, who was an excellent farmer, was a poor judge of stock. He used to leave the selling of his cattle and pigs to men who came to the farm and took the stock away to Romford, or some other market, and sold it on commission. Many farmers followed this practice in those days, and also attended the local market at Chelmsford themselves. One of these commission agents was a well-known character. He invariably made the same remark when looking at a fat beast or hog. 'That's a good beast,' he would say, 'and who knows if I don't?'

My grandfather had a good figure, and looked well on a horse, on which he rode about the farms, while my grandmother drove about the country lanes in a little pony chaise with a snow-white pony. So we can leave them: grandmother in her chaise, and grandfather on his horse, trotting beside her, as away they go, out of the farmyard gate, and down the lane past the chestnut-trees.

CHAPTER III

SCHOOLDAYS

WHEN he was ten years old father was sent to school in Chelmsford. The school was a large private house in the Springfield Road, run by a Mr. Hunt, and was in consequence called Hunt's School.

Mr. Hunt, who was stone blind, was assisted by his wife and a Mr. Nichols. Father says he progressed well in his studies, except in French, which was taught by Mrs. Hunt. He usually finished French lessons outside the classroom door.

Mrs. Hunt had definite ideas on health. In fact, her maxim might be described as 'gregory, gregory all the way.' Of the forty boys in the school only about twelve were boarded, and they were kept thoroughly purged. Once, when there was an epidemic of measles in the town, father felt ill one morning, and was unwise enough to tell Mrs. Hunt about it. She gave him three-quarters of a pint of gregory-powder. Luckily he had some dry biscuits in his pocket, which helped him through. He did not get measles.

The boys were bathed two at a time in an old wooden

kneading trough. One can imagine Mrs. Hunt stopping up the cracks with putty before she filled it up on bath night.

The food at this establishment, where father seems to have been happy enough, was undoubtedly very bad indeed. The staple item was rice and treacle. This would have been all right in moderation had not Mr. Hunt, who, no doubt, found forty boys' fees no great income, bought cattle treacle and chicken rice as a way out of his difficulties. This was sometimes varied by treacle pudding, which was regarded by his scholars with even deeper horror. One unfortunate boy, named Bertie Baker, found his helping of the stuff quite uneatable one day at lunch. It was returned to him at tea, and again at supper. He managed to eat it next morning at breakfast. An understanding maid had scattered a little brown sugar on it, which, he said, made all the difference. Mostly, however, they got it safely into their pockets. I suppose that is why my father never to this day puts his hands into any of his pockets except to put something in or take something out.

Sometimes when the boys had some pocket-money they helped out this meagre allowance at a small sweet shop near by, kept by an old woman called Sally Gladwin. Here for a sixpence deposited on the counter you could eat as much and as many as you would of the cheap sweets she provided, but could take nothing away to eat at your leisure. While the boys were gorging themselves, and gradually beginning to feel that they couldn't possibly eat their money's worth, Sally Gladwin stood behind the counter, eagle-eyed, chanting at regular intervals: 'Eat what you like and pocket none!'

As a variant to this father and another boy would share a penny loaf of bread and a penn'orth of cheese. Father said that this latter way of helping out Mr. Hunt's rations was preferable. You didn't feel so sick afterwards.

Old blind Mr. Hunt made a great favourite of father, and

every morning after school father used to accompany him to his study and read the *Daily Telegraph* leader out aloud to him. In return for this sterling service he was always given half a pint of beer. Sometimes father led old Mr. Hunt about the town, and when he had safely led him to the 'Saracen's Head,' or the 'George' (long since vanished) in Duke Street, he would be dismissed with a penny or two to spend, and told to come back again in half an hour or so's time.

'I've got a little business to do in here, my boy,' said Mr. Hunt, feeling for the handle of the door into the saloon bar; 'you run along and come back for me later.'

When father had been here for two years he was taken away and sent to a school at Tottenham, which went by the striking name of the Eagle House College, and was run by an old gentleman called Dr. Fernandez. He also made a great favourite of father, who had a knack in those days of tapping the fountain at its head.

The amount of work father did here seems to have been rather a minus quantity, but he was prepared for confirmation, and confirmed at St. Paul's Cathedral. This has given him a fatherly interest in the cathedral, which is the only one in England he enters willingly just to have a look round. Though he is a regular churchgoer, and was churchwarden for forty years at West Hanningfield, he reached a state of sublime boredom on the seventh or eighth day of a tour of English cathedrals, which we did by car some years ago. When, at Gloucester Cathedral, he was hurried by an officious usher out of a side-chapel which he had entered inadvertently while a service was in progress, he returned to the car and went to sleep. After that he just stood outside cathedral after cathedral, and said:

'Yes, that's a fine building. Must have taken a lot of labour to build it!'

To return to the Eagle House College. The main sport,

or any way the one father seems to have enjoyed most, was paper-chasing. Father was the hare more often than not, and usually took the same two boys with him to carry the bags of paper, one a Frenchman called Delange, and the other one Tommy Ibbetson. The classic run of all time was when the three went right through the Alexandra Palace and made a five-mile point. The hounds lost them completely, and they arrived back at the school late that evening, having traversed all the purlieus of Edmonton, tired, happy, and triumphant.

The boys seem to have been pretty tough on the whole. During father's second Christmas term several of them decided on a celebration. The knotty problem apparently was whether to have whisky or rum. Father, rising fifteen, and possibly hoping to keep the party within bounds, timidly suggested a bottle of gin. This was immediately dismissed as 'an old woman's drink'!

In the end it was whisky, but the party passed off quietly on the whole. The boys had to go in to prayers soon after. They got through them all right, but had some anxious moments over a boy named Marte, who developed a tendency to chime in with Dr. Fernandez during the prayers.

Dr. Fernandez, who was a genial soul, picked on father to look after his greenhouse fire in the evening. I suppose he was chosen because he came of farming stock. Father doesn't seem to have had too satisfactory a stewardship, as the greenhouse caught fire one night after he had given it some more than usually enthusiastic stoking; and he also helped himself to the good doctor's apples, which were stored in a shed near by. However, the fire was not severe, and father's depredations on the apples were never too heavy, and he retained the honourable post of stoker to the day he left.

Fernandez's satellites were rather a mixed bag. One named Havelin was very popular with the boys, being good at games, and possessing a great sense of humour. Another named Batty was the complete reverse. Father just calls him a 'miserable devil'; and he was nicknamed 'Nabob' after a brand of sour pickle. Once, after suffering weeks of sniping from pea-shooters, Nabob caught several boys planning how they would 'pick him off' through the key-hole of his classroom door. Having caught them he flogged them in one of the lavatories. Such cramped quarters must have spoilt his execution.

When the boys left at the end of each term Dr. Fernandez shook hands with each one, wishing them 'Happy holidays and many on 'em'; or 'Happy Christmas and many on 'em.'

Father always adds 'many on 'em' to his good wishes to this day. He shook hands with Dr. Fernandez for the last time at Christmas time 1876, and went home to work at the age of fourteen years and eight months.

CHAPTER IV

THE YOUNG HORSEMAN

THE ice crackled sharply in the ruts and puddles as father hurried along by grandfather's side on the morning of New Year's Day, 1877. It was just seven o'clock, and the moon still shone with that steely sharpness which it has on frosty mornings just before dawn.

Father's fingers were blue with cold, and would be colder, for they were going swede pulling, and pulling swedes with the frost on them is no joke. He thrust his hands deep into his pockets. Grandfather, whose blood was beginning to circulate, looked at him and smiled.

'You'll feel better presently, John,' he said. 'Remember you haven't had breakfast this year yet.'

This incident, after a few days' holiday at Christmas, was the curtain-raiser to father's working life, and grandfather certainly gave him a good grounding in the 'art and practice of farming.'

In March he was put to help an old henchman, George Snell, with drilling some blue peas in Flat Field Ten Acres, called for short 'th' owd flat.' Father proved a ready pupil, and half-way through the morning Snell thought him far

enough advanced to be left in charge while he slipped home
for something to wash the dust out of his throat, it being
a dry March that year.

Things went well for a time, but father omitted to put
the 'drill-press' on hard enough, with the result that some
of the seed lay uncovered on the ground. What George
said to father when he came back cannot, unfortunately,
be written here, but if anybody wants to know they can
come and ask father. He remembers quite distinctly.

Later that spring father went sowing clover seed by
hand, again with George Snell. George was determined
to take it out of his pupil, and went up and down the field
as fast as he could go. Father's and George's rapid progress attracted the attention of one of the old village
worthies. He leant over the field gate and watched them
for some time, and then went back to the 'Ivy House,'
where he duly reported the incident.

'Oi saw young Smith and owd George Snell a-broadcastin' clover seed. They were a-gooin' up and down that
field like steamers in the Thames.

That harvest father drove the wagons from the corn-
fields to the stacks, and later on when threshing began in
October he drove cart-loads of oats from Partridge's Farm
to the big barns at Link House, himself loading and un-
loading the oats, which weigh twelve stones a sack.

In the late spring of 1878 over two hundred sheep were
clipped in the big barn at Link House. The work was done
by a gang of six men from a neighbouring village, who tra-
velled the county during the spring and early summer, washing and clipping sheep. About a fortnight before the time
arranged for clipping they would come to Link House and
wash the sheep in the pond at the bottom of the farmyard.
Then, at the appointed time arranged between the men and
grandfather, the sheep would be shut up on Sunday night,
and any one who knows sheep will realize that those who

slept on the side of the house nearest to the barn didn't get much sleep that night. The men were in the barn and had started clipping by five o'clock on Monday morning, and by the evening most of the sheep were shorn and let out into the meadows, save an unhappy remnant which the men left to finish on Tuesday morning before going on to the next farm and another flock.

That hay-time grandfather bought a new Hornby grass-mower, which father fetched from Chelmsford, and drove all the season. He was suffering badly from vast numbers of boils at this time, and he always says Job had nothing on him that hay-time. Pad the iron seat of the mower as he might, he still couldn't forget them. However, by harvest the worst was over and, after an argument with grandfather, father got out and used an old 'Burgess and Key' reaper, which had been laid up in the cart-lodge since 1870, when grandfather bought it. He had had a great deal of trouble with it then, and had packed it up in disgust, and returned to the gangs of reapers who, though slow and thirsty, were reliable.

George Pammerton, who had driven the old Burgess in 1870, didn't like father resurrecting it. He said he didn't know why, if he couldn't make it go right years ago, father should be able to now. It was a very light machine, and a proper bone-shaker. Father drove it with two horses at length in front, and after cutting a field of beans and a field of barley, smashed it up fairly thoroughly. It made a come-back again the following year, when father tried driving it with the horses side by side. This seemed to balance it better, and he really got some work done with it.

That harvest marked the beginning of the worst period father remembers in weather and farming conditions. Rain fell day after day, until the corn grew in the traves, and when at last the weather broke for a day or two the farmers carted their corn still damp in a desperate attempt

to save some of it before the rain began again. Grandfather carted some barley which was unfit; it spoiled in the
stacks, and was virtually useless for any purpose whatsoever.

However, most of the corn was eventually gathered and,
the weather improving, the winter corn was sown in good
conditions. Grandfather ploughed the land at Link House
in half-rod stretches, and father struck up the furrows with
two horses.

The bad times began to make themselves felt when the
corn came to be threshed, for it yielded badly, and as the
hay-time had also been what father calls 'tetchy,' little good
hay had been made.

With a wet hay-time and harvest still in the future, grandfather gave a dance for his two eldest daughters, Sophie and
Kate, at Link House in May. Grandfather being a very
generous man, and grandmother a very efficient woman,
the evening was a great success.

In 1879 father took all responsibility for the drilling on
the six hundred and twenty-five acres of Link House and
the other farms. The weather, which had broken again in
November, remained bad, and father was still drilling wheat
in January. All the spring corn was sown in the worst
possible conditions, which left little hope of a better harvest
to help with last year's losses.

There was one famous day in 1879 which father still
quotes whenever he thinks we are being more than usually
slow with getting the dung on the land.

'Why,' he says, 'I remember one day George Pammerton
and I had five men filling the dung carts in the bullock
yard, and we shot one hundred and five loads on seven
acres!'

You need to have personal experience of dung-carting
really to appreciate that anecdote.

Hay-time again gave no relief. The horses shied at the
water standing in the grass as father drove them in one of

the meadows near the brook which threaded the farm. He left that field and cut another, and returned to find the water had fallen. He cut the grass, which was, having been practically immersed, of little value. The weather held for a day or two, and the hay was made and cocked. Then the rain came again steadily and incessantly. The brook began to rise, and soon the haycocks were floating away down the valley.

Harvest was no better, and was long and protracted, continuing into October. As a watery harvest moon shone down over the muddy stubble, the wagons creaked slowly towards the stack yard. Three horses to each wagon, straining in their harness. The wheat and barley in many cases yielded only three sacks to the acre.

Many farmers were unable to bear this continued loss, farms began to stand empty, and farm sales became more and more frequent. These farms were not allowed to stand vacant for long. Scots farmers began to come south and, buying the land cheap, to settle with their families in farms, which, in many cases, had previously been farmed by the same family for hundreds of years. The Scots worked hard, and so did their families, and they employed less labour.

The year 1879 marked the beginning of the end for the real old-time farmer, with his large numbers of labourers and easy-going life. Labourers in 1879 were earning twelve shillings a week, and for them the distress was not so acute. Existence in any case was a hard business, and they were used to it.

In this critical period my grandmother's tongue became sharper, and she raised large numbers of chickens and turkeys, with which the children were made to help. Grandfather was worried and silent. He met the landlord, Badeley, in Chelmsford, and told him that the rent must be reduced or remain unpaid. It was reduced. The

Church of England woke to the seriousness of the situation, and many parsons gave some relief by consenting to a ten per cent reduction in tithe.

There were eight children to feed that winter at Link House, and things looked bad for the farm, unless the weather soon began to improve. Winter started early with sharp frosts, and father was still drilling wheat in December.

One day he and George Cox were drilling with a slight coat of snow on the ground. Father had some cold tea and bread and cheese in his basket, and grandfather sent some beer at midday. It was cold standing under the hedge with the snow coming in light flurries, and the horses with their nosebags on were steaming slightly. Lunch was a short meal in these conditions. That night George Cox came to Link House and initiated father into the mysteries of brewing.

The water for brewing was carried from the well in pails, and filled a large tub in the brew house; from this in turn the large copper, holding a hogshead, was filled with a jet. Then followed a long series of boiling and cooling with relays of water, the whole process taking some considerable time, and father said that by morning you'd had about enough. This was allowed to make no difference to the next day's work, however.

After a few nights of tuition by George Cox, father was left to brew on his own, and he still shudders a little when he tells the story of how he once went to sleep and woke in the early dawn to find the copper fire nearly out. He worked feverishly, but was still in the thick of things when grandfather came down in the morning. When grandfather said, suspiciously, that he was a bit behind, father said briefly that he had had a job with the copper flues. He never went to sleep again.

On New Year's Day 1880 a violent thunderstorm swept across Essex, leaving the fields a sea of mud. It caught the

Father, aged about thirty

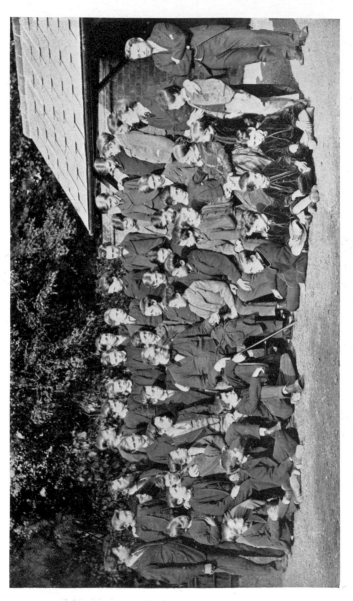

Hunt's School, 1872. Father, bottom left, front row, aged ten

Link House

Our last harvest at Link House.   Family group, 1921.
Back: Cousins and Aunt.   Front: Mother, Author, Father

Silas Pledger and Father
Old Lodge, Springfield, 1928

Father and Mother
Hill House, Broomfield, 1937

Grandfather
Edward Alfred Smith

Grandmother
Annie Channon Smith

Father
Hill Farm, Broomfield, 1935

Harry Cox, Stockman
Hill Farm, Broomfield

Sam Tyler
'Farmer'

George Cox
'Butty'

men out drilling in the fields, and one loud crash of thunder frightened the horses on the drill. The off-wheeler broke his harness and bolted. Late that night he reappeared at Link House, muddied and chastened, but quite whole.

This was the weather's last fling, and the rest of that January was lovely. A popular wheat much sown at this time went by the poetic name of 'Taunton Dene.' Considerably better than many of our present wheats which are getting names like 'Million 3,' and sound more like chemistry than agriculture.

The fallows made in 1879 were full of twitch, which the village women were given eightpence a day for pulling and leaving in heaps for burning. This must have been worse than that other back-breaking and heart-breaking job invented by farmers of those days, stone-picking.

After hay-time was over father was sent to plough till harvest. Every morning he was up at five, and going down the back stairs to the red-tiled kitchen, he would find a loaf of home-made bread with a jug of cold tea by the back door. He would break off the top of the loaf and cut a small hole in the middle of it. Into this went a bit of butter. Then he put back the top of the loaf, picked up the cold tea, and away out for the day.

He had to go to the small off-hand farm called Partridges, three fields away from Link House, to get his horses. Their nosebags were filled for the midday feed, and slung on the collar seals. Then on to the back of one, with the other's lead rein in one hand, and away out for the day's ploughing in, perhaps, 'Bloodlands' or the 'Owd Flat.'

Occasionally father was lucky, and would be ploughing a field next to the road when old Joe Cox, an old pedlar with a donkey cart, went by. Joe Cox's goods covered a very wide field, from drapery to fish, and father bought many a pint of winkles at threepence a pint, varied by two or three bloaters. If he had bought bloaters he would wait

B

till 'bait' or 'bever' time came and then, having hung on the horses' nosebags, he would light a little fire under the hedge and proceed to cook the bloaters on a sharp stick. He says that he has never had a meal to touch those he had that summer ploughing, but that they could have been improved with beer instead of cold tea.

Father remembers the following autumn because his horses were used for carting bricks for a new cow shed, and he was put on to clear a field of mangold during a heavy frost. Grandfather always had his roots cleared during frost, if possible, owing to a mistaken idea that it improved their quality. What always happened was that as soon as the frost broke all the mangolds rotted, and the clamps remained whited sepulchres for a while until they caved in. Any one who has worked with frozen root crops will know why father remembers that autumn.

On 1st December grandfather went to Ingatestone Fair and, after having his pocket picked, bought twelve bullocks. As soon as these were brought home they developed foot-and-mouth disease, but as this was before it became notifiable, there was nothing to worry about. They were put in a warm yard and kept well littered, and dosed with one pound of salts apiece, mixed with a little ginger.

The whole bunch recovered, and made lovely bullocks, but it must have been a warm morning's work roping twelve bullocks and dosing them.

The beginning of 1881 is memorable for the great snow-storm on 18th January. It was a still grey frosty morning, and the wagons went off to Chelmsford with loads of wheat for the mill as usual. About nine o'clock it started to snow slowly and then with gradually increasing force. The farm buildings could not be seen from the house. The wind, full east, soon began to drift the snow. One of the wagoners on his way home drove into someone's park at Great Baddow, and only with difficulty got back on to the road again. Finally he and many others drew up their wagons and carts by the side of the road, and made their way home across the fields as best they could in the blinding snow. They were glad to get back into the stables that night, and bed and feed the horses, with the lantern throwing an uneven yellow light, and the snow swirling in over the half stable door.

Father chose this bright airy day to go rabbiting with William Benson, but met with only moderate success, as might have been expected. However, as a test of endurance it takes a bit of beating. He took a long time getting home, falling into drifts, and walking with snow up to his knees in places. Near the village school he walked headlong into a gentleman returning from a happy evening at the 'Ivy House,' and knocked him flying into a drift. After father had helped him out, he suddenly became truculent, and wanted to fight. Father gave him a gentle push back into the drift, and continued on his way.

The snow ceased suddenly the next morning about nine o'clock, and grandfather promptly set the men to work to clear the chase leading from the farm to the main road. His first idea was labour-saving, but inefficient. All the horses were led out of the stables and each provided with a rider, and then, led by father, also mounted, they proceeded to walk the horses up and down the chase on top of the drifts in the faint but enduring hope of trampling down a path.

The effort was unsuccessful, and the snow had to be cleared by hand. Father said that while the horses were being ridden up and down the lane it looked like a succession of bad starts for the 'Farmyard Stakes.'

Grandfather was given the job of seeing that all the roads in the West Hanningfield district were cleared of snow, and soon the village was communicating again with the outer world. Many of the large drifts, however, lay on the roadsides and in the ditches till the beginning of April.

Rain and floods followed the snow, and were followed in turn by a lovely late spring. On 7th May father was drilling grass seeds in Ten Acres at Cannon Barns. As he drove the drill up and down the field he saw grandfather walking slowly across the burrows towards him. Father stopped the drill, and spoke to him for a few minutes. It was the last time grandfather walked over the land he loved. A slight cold he had that day developed into pneumonia, and he died a fortnight later, on 21st May 1881.

CHAPTER V

MARKET TOWN

As his palfrey splashed through the shallow water and scrambled up the bank of the river, Bishop Maurice viewed his drabbled robes with distaste. For he was Bishop of London, and in the year of grace 1130 made his tours of the diocese in full regalia and with a considerable retinue. The mud was drying thick on the hem of his robes. It was, he thought, high time there was a bridge built over this river Can. The Chelmer, near by, had a good ford, but here a bridge was needed. He himself would see to it; and not only did he see to it that a bridge was erected, but in the same year he founded the market which ever since has flourished at Chelmsford. For this bridge brought the great road from London to Colchester directly through the town, instead of passing round to the west by Writtle, as it had done.

Chelmsford lies in a valley almost in the centre of Essex, at the joining of the Chelmer and the Can; and its market, in father's younger days, was held in the High Street of the town. The High Street is dominated by the shire hall, a massive building, with a front of white stone ornamented with four Ionic columns.   To the right lies Tindal Square, and from here, running up to the station, is Duke Street.

My grandmother thought poorly of the High Street market.   There were holes let in along the pavements, so that posts could be erected on market days, to which the cattle could be tied.

The populace picked its way carefully along the pavements, and, as grandmother said, the cattle could add considerable hazards to the normal shopping round.

The horse sale was held on the left-hand side of the street near the 'Saracen's Head,' and here old Mr. George Hilliard, the auctioneer, would retail the merits of many a 'good worker, sound in wind and limb, and quiet in all gears.'   As he talked the horse would be run up and down before his stand, while the crowd surged backwards and forwards, and the crack of the whip came intermittently to liven up the lot under the hammer.

The spring and winter fairs, on 12th May and 12th November respectively, must have given even more zest to the scene, for then there would be greatly increased entries of stock, and in Tindal Square stood the roundabouts and shooting galleries.

It was not surprising therefore that the landlord of the 'Saracen's Head' earnestly requested father not to send his wagons to the inn on market or fair days.   For father, in his early farming time, supplied the 'Saracen's Head' with loads of wheat straw, and the returning wagons would be loaded with dung from the inn stables.   The wagons, loaded high with straw, were unable to pass under the 'Saracen's' archway, and half each load had to be dumped on the pavement and carried down afterwards.   On top of market-day crowds, and with the horse sale just outside, the straw arriving was just a bit too much, the landlord said.

Though the market-day visitor might have a long thirsty

'Saracen's Head' and Tindal Statue, Chelmsford

journey he was, at least, well provided for when he reached Chelmsford.　Mr. William White records that in 1848 there were forty-six 'Hotels, Inns, and Taverns' and thirty-four 'Beer-houses.'　Certainly hospitality to suit every taste was to be found.

Tindal Square was previously known as Conduit Square, because before the present statue of Judge Tindal was erected a conduit stood in the centre.　The conduit was supplied by a pipe-line from Burgess Well Spring some four hundred yards away, and from the yawning mouths of four lions water ran continuously.　It formed a stream which ran to the corner of the square, and then diverged, one branch running on down the right side of the High Street, and the other crossing the street to just below the 'Saracen's Head,' before continuing its journey down the town.　The streams must, one feels, have added still more to the hazards of market day.

The stream ran conveniently for laying the dust in the High Street on hot summer days, and the old man who had this job was a real expert at his work.　His equipment consisted of a bundle of old bags and a large wooden maltster's shovel, rounded at the edges.　Laying the bags in the stream as a dam, he would wait till a fair-sized pool of water had collected, and then, dipping the great wooden shovel deeply, he would send a very considerable sheet of water flying across the street.

From their nursery window in the private house next to the 'Saracen's Head' two little boys watched this performance with great enjoyment.　For this afternoon a gang of small boys were following the old dust-layer, and throwing stones and half bricks into the stream so that the water splashed all over him.　The onlookers in the nursery stood fascinated, for the old man continued his work apparently utterly unaware of the riot of noise and splashes around him.　Slowly he dropped his bags and stood waiting while the dammed water gathered into a large deep pool. The splashes grew larger and the mirth of his tormentors uncontrollable. Suddenly the old man moved. The pool was full now and, dipping his shovel, he sent one of the best sheets of water he had ever thrown in his life flying over his enemies. Then another, and another, before the urchins, soaked and utterly surprised, could gather their wits, and run howling away up the High Street!

"'Course,' the old man would say in answer to inquiries about his work, 'that don't do to goo chuckin' that water anywhere. You got to keep yer eye up for the ladies and gentlemen.'

The two spectators in the nursery turned back to their game. A good game it was that afternoon, but a poor substitute for the wonderful scene they had just been watching. They were playing tents. It was their nurse's afternoon out, and they had borrowed her spare crinoline frame. Placed under the nursery table and covered with a rug or two it made somewhere about the most satisfactory tent they had ever erected.

It would not be many years ahead before their father, Mr. Wykeham Chancellor, would be first Mayor of Chelmsford, for it was in 1888 that the old market town was made a borough.

Every one knew old Mrs. Apple French's shop on the corner of Conduit Square and High Street. Scarcely bigger than a hen-coop it was. Every morning Mrs. French, as red-cheeked as her apples, would come bustling in from the country with her stock, and somehow manage to squeeze both them and herself into the very limited space available and then sit beaming all day upon her customers.

Walking on from Mrs. French's munching an apple the idle loiterer might cross the square and make his way up Duke Street, which was then the town's fashionable quarter, and consisted almost entirely of comfortable dwelling-houses.

*B

There perhaps he might pass the tall elegant figure of old Mr. Chievely, very popular amongst his friends, but never quite living down an old joke. For Mr. Chievely had belonged to the militia but, for some obscure reason known only to himself, had not accompanied them on their journey to the Crimea some years before, and his friends still pulled his leg about it.

Crimean veterans were objects of great interest and veneration for the younger generation. Young Chancellor, returning from school for the holidays, reported to his parents that at half-term an old one-legged soldier had come to sit outside the school gates. The boys might inspect his stump and touch the bullet embedded in his scalp for tuppence.

To the left of the High Street lies the small island known historically as Mesopotamia. It is caused by a branching of the Chelmer just before its junction with the Can, and was once the scene of the Mesopotamia election. This was a mock election, which was apparently held to amuse the people while a real election was in progress. Mr. William White quotes from some unknown source that 'every accommodation is provided for the candidates and their friends,' and 'the committee sit daily in the vicinity of the hustings.' He then goes on to recount that 'when the poll is open the candidates parade the streets on horse-back, each attended by a page; and at the close, the members elected for this "peculiar jurisdiction" are chaired through the town, on men's shoulders; and afterwards ducked in the river. The honour of immersion is also conferred on the unsuccessful candidates; and the important business of the day is concluded by breaking the chairs. The mock election of 1830, afforded an unusual display of wit and oratory; and the Mesopotamia candidates were not less the objects of popular applause than the more learned gentlemen of whom they were typical!'

From which it would seem that Mr. White had not too high an opinion of the said 'learned gentlemen.' It seems probable that candidates for Mesopotamian honours were rather few and far between if polling day fell in a spell of cold weather.

When the new market was opened in the late seventies below Tindal Square the old farmers grumbled for a time. You didn't know where to find anybody, they said, and they found the business of settling up their accounts in the newly erected counting house a dreary business after their accustomed cheerful settlements in the 'White Hart' or the 'Saracen's Head.'

When father was first taken to market by grandfather he was taken into the 'White Hart' at the end of the day while grandfather had his 'usual.' All round sat the farmers, with their long churchwarden pipes and glasses of grog beside them. What matter if one or two did make too good a night of it? They had good horses to take them home, and quiet roads to drive on.

However, those with wives and families must hurry back at the arranged time to their governess carts and gigs, now piled high with parcels. Then up under the echoing arch of, perhaps, the 'Saracen's Head,' off down the High Street, and out into the country lanes, heads well down against the rain on winter evenings, or else glancing backwards or forwards over the hedge tops in consideration of neighbours' crops in fine spring or summer weather; and so home till next week.

J.K.Popham

CHAPTER VI

THE VILLAGE SCENE

It often seems that our much-vaunted modern civilization, with its high speeds and super-efficiency, has robbed us of much that was of real value. As recently as forty years ago men still found great joy in simple pleasures and their daily work and managed to get along pretty well without the wireless, the cinema, and the daily village bus. That these and the many other modern amenities are wonderful things cannot be denied, but sometimes their noisy and speedy arrival obscured many aspects of the old village and country life which then began quietly to disappear.

Harvest, for example, was in those days a ceremony, and not just the period of hard work that it has become to-day. The day before reaping started the men would be allowed the day off and, taking a wagon with a pair of horses, drive to the nearest brewery to buy their harvest beer, most of the men bringing back an eighteen-gallon cask, and some a 'thirty-sixer.' Back would come the wagon with its cheering load and, by then, hilarious passengers. At each man's cottage his barrel would be unloaded and tapped. This, of course, entailed one all round and, if the party was a large one, the horses usually took the wagon home on their own initiative; and the horseman was apt to find his harness in rather unlikely spots when he got to the stable next morning.

During harvest any one who came on the farm was fair game for 'largess.' This was an established custom, and any farmer, merchant, or traveller would be met with the demand:

'What about largess, master?'

He thereupon forked out his florin or half-dollar, and all subscriptions were saved up for the end of harvest. It is easy to imagine the slowly sauntering horseman who 'just happened' to be crossing the yard as a stranger drove up to the farmhouse.

In the old days before the reapers really came in to use, the reaper gang would take their work at so much an acre, and the foreman, or 'Lord of the Harvest,' as the leading man was often called, would be paid at the end of the harvest. It was then the invariable custom to adjourn to the nearest pub to share out. This share out sometimes took place on the same night as the harvest supper provided by 'the master' for his workers.

There is a good story of a gang in father's early days that adjourned, after a heavy day's cutting, to the 'Plough and Sail.' Beer was cheap, closing time happily non-existent, and by the time the cash ran out the journey home was a hopeless impossibility. However, it was a hot August night, and a circuitous journey brought the revellers to the scene of their day's work, where they settled down for the night. One of the gang, more altruistic or possibly drunker than the rest, took off his coat and waistcoat, and laid them lovingly over the sleeping form of one of his companions. He discovered his mistake after an hour or so, but, rather than withdraw his fine gesture, spent the chilly dawn hours walking up and down the field, trying to keep warm.

Early next morning father was confronted by the altruistic reaper's distraught wife, and the information that the gang had spent the night out. He promptly rode over to the field, but found the gang hard at work and none the worse. Father never even spoke to them, just turned his horse and rode away.

Often in a hot dry harvest, when the moon was full, the men would go on carting long after the moon was up, and, in the dim silvery light, as the huge loads creaked slowly up the lane, the men would sing old long-forgotten songs, that carried far over the still fields and woods, and let their wives know they 'd soon be home and wanting their suppers.

When the horsemen had to make long journeys, say, perhaps from West Hanningfield to Rayne, near Braintree, with a load of hay, they would have everything loaded and ready the night before, and be driving their wagon out of the farm gates by half-past four in the morning, and passing through the still quiet streets of Chelmsford by six. One of father's horsemen, named Sam Tyler, often fetched loads of soot from Chelmsford, and for this duty had a special suit, of which the most outstanding feature was a brown velvet waistcoat with red buttons. Sam was extremely what might be described as 'horse proud,' and one May morning as he drove past Baddow brewery people standing on the side of the road called out to compliment him on his turnout. The chestnut-trees were in blossom, and the sun shone brilliantly on the dappled coats of his pair, and was reflected back from their shining coats and harness, while their manes and long full tails were tied up with many-coloured ribbons.

On Good Friday this same Sam Tyler, along with all the other horsemen, followed an invariable custom. Work was started an hour earlier, at five o'clock, and finished for the day at ten. It must have been an uneasy business, for they went to work in their better clothes, and then went straight from work to church. If they failed to appear at church, they lost the day's pay, so the rector was always gratified by a very full congregation. With wages at eleven shillings per week, ten shillings for the missus and one shilling for beer and baccy, a day's pay is not lightly to be thrown away. After the service Sam would come home, have a sound sleep, a meal, washed down by half a pint of home-made wine, and then away out to 'wood-cart.' All the wood in the hedges cut down by the farmer during the winter belonged by right to him; all, that is, except the old thorn stubs which were known as 'runters' and were the hedger's privilege. The waste wood which was not good enough to make into proper faggots, the hedger made into 'scrap faggots,' and these too were his. Nearly all farmers would also 'give' a hedge to any man who wanted to cut it down in his spare time. In this case, of course, all the wood belonged to the man.

On this same day, if Easter was late, and the primroses out, the children would gather large bunches in the woods and take them to the church for the Easter decorations, where they were each given a hot cross bun to take home for tea. At Christmas time, too, in my grandfather's day, a bullock or pig was usually killed at Link House, and each man went home on Christmas Eve with a hunk of meat and a gallon of beer.

There were several different ways in which the labourer's wife augmented the bread, pork, and vegetables which formed the staple items of the family diet. A few young

rooks in early May, skinned and made into rook pie, were
considered a rare delicacy, though little beside the breasts
were eatable.   Later, if your husband happened to be the
shepherd, or a friend of the shepherd's, a lambs'-tail pie
was To-day's Special.   The tails were skinned, soaked, and
then stewed, and finally made into a pie, extremely rich and
full of jelly.   Of course, if you were a patient woman and
your husband was a member of the sparrow club, an occasional sparrow pie could be used to vary the diet.   The
sparrows were plucked (a considerable business, unless a
large family could be turned on to it), and then cooked
whole.   Bonier than the boniest fish, the meat was good,
what there was of it and if you could find any, and the
gravy rich and nourishing.

The good housewife also had at her command an endless
variety of home-made wines, which could mostly be made
easily and cheaply.   Starting at one end of the scale with
elderberry, and ranging through blackberry, orange, dande-
lion, carrot, beetroot, and potato, to mangold, there was
no end to the possible flavours and types.   While an occasional daring spirit with a palate for the unusual would
make hips-and-haws wine, a good brew of which was
regarded by the best connoisseurs as a 'very sound wine.'

The method of making mangold wine is a pretty fair
example of the production of these country wines.   The
mangold is first thoroughly scrubbed and dried, and then
left for a day or two to wilt.   The next stage is to cut up the
mangold and boil slowly for six hours, using eight gallons
of water to produce two gallons of wine.   To add kick and
flavour a little ginger in a muslin bag and an ounce of hops
may be added if procurable.   When the boiling is finished,
strain off the juice into a pan containing eight pounds of
sugar and the juice of three oranges and two lemons.   This
is left to cool, and then bottled up, though in the case of most
wines a little yeast should be added to make them 'work.'

Rhubarb wine is an exception, being extremely lively, and liable to burst a bottle at any time. All wines should be kept at least six months, and should be approached and drunk with care. For occasionally a more than usually potent vintage strikes the good cottager's guest unaware, and sends him home 'unsteadily to bed.'

In those days, when to meet an ex-soldier brought memories of the Crimea, and the Boer War was a cloud no larger than a man's hand on the horizon, life had an even tenor that permitted of much time and labour being expended on work and objects that to-day would be considered waste of time and money. Stone-picking is a fair example. Women and their families would go stone-picking at the rate of a penny farthing per bushel. They would make large heaps of stones about the fields, which would be picked up later and used to repair stackyards or farm lanes. The stone-picker's lament was that however many stones were picked off a field one year, there were just as many the next, and after a time it broke even the keenest picker's heart.

To women, of course, fell the duty of gleaning. In the old days at West Hanningfield a bell would be rung night and morning for gleaning to start and stop. The bent figures dotted over the wheat etches are an almost forgotten sight. The custom survived the first inefficient reapers, but with the introduction of the first modern binders, and the use of a horse rake to gather any corn left lying in the fields, the gleaners wandered disconsolate for a year or so, and then gave it up. Rising wages and an improved standard of living also removed the need to obtain flour for the winter.

Gleaning had its own etiquette, and strict method of procedure. No one might start to glean till the last sheaf had been carted off the field, and if, for any reason, a farmer wanted to keep the gleaners out of one of his fields, he would tell his men to leave one trave standing, and the field, till that trave finally disappeared, was 'taboo' to the gleaners. If the field was to be left quiet for the partridges to feed before a shooting day, small twigs were stuck in the ground to warn the gleaners off; and in any case they had to wait for the sun to get up and dry the dew before they started work.

The women would pick up the corn stalks till they had formed a fair-sized sheaf, and then tie it up. Each woman formed her own trave, and marked it with an article of clothing or piece of greenery, so that no 'pirate' gleaner would descend and lay claim to it. Round their waists the women carried a 'short-ear tray,' which was a small bag carried in front of the gleaner, and into it was put anything too short to go into the sheaf.

At the end of the day, when the gleaners' curfew tolled out over the fields, the women went back to their little traves, and cut all the ears of corn off the stalks, put them in a bag, and carried them home. The next step was taken when the threshing machine visited the farm. The labourer carried his bags of wheat ears to the farm in the morning, and when a stack had been finished it was put through the machine, and that night he carried home his corn. If he happened to be a horseman, or one of his mates was, he waited till the next load of wheat went to the mill, and then took his gleaned corn along. On his next journey he would pick up the flour, while the miller kept the middlings and bran as payment. Before machine threshing was introduced, and two men would spend an entire winter in one of the barns threshing with flails, it was just a question of doing their own corn after the day's work was done. Many families obtained enough flour by this means to keep them right through the winter.

Many of the cottages had large deep brick ovens, and the women baked their own bread, sending a child across the fields to Baddow brewery the day before for a penn'orth of yeast. Any one who has eaten the old cottage loaves always says there is nothing to touch them nowadays. The children on baking days were given 'paddles,' little pieces of bread left over and put in the oven beside the loaf; crusty and crisp, with a little bit of butter inside, they were delicious.

Children in those days were undoubtedly tough. They had to be. At a very tender age they were put to pig- and sheep-tending to prevent animals straying too far when turned into unfenced fields, and from this they graduated to rook-scaring. Out in the fields all day with a piece of bread and cheese for lunch, and a huge pair of wooden clappers, they earned their shilling a week. Another activity for which they joyously stayed away from school was 'driving away.' This was when a gang was clearing a bullock yard of dung, and the child of perhaps seven or nine would drive the full carts to the field which was having a 'coat of muck,' and bring the empty carts back again. There was another job which the children did not enjoy, and that was helping their father at 'land-ditching.' In the old days land was drained far better than it is to-day, and it was all done by hand. When the land was stiff clay under the subsoil, the boy's duty was to soften the earth with water as the spade went down for the second 'spit' of earth below the top soil. With a little tin on the end of a short pole, which was kept replenished from a nearby bucket, the boy endlessly moistened the earth as the man's spade stuck in the hard clay. Father remembers seeing miserable little boys at this work, blue with cold, and with their hands covered with chilblains. This purgatory must have more than discounted the joys of 'driving away.'

When the land-ditch pipes were laid they were usually covered with a layer of cockle shells before the trench was filled up, to help percolation and prevent earth getting easily into the pipes and silting them up. These cockle shells were carted from Leigh-on-Sea, near Southend, and many of the drains they were put in would be running now if the ditches into which they had outlet were cleared.

Guy Fawkes night saw the young bloods in West Hanningfield and the neighbouring villages out on the loose. Most of them managed to buy a firework or two, and all of them had musical instruments, from concertinas and mouth-organs to penny whistles. From house to house went this assorted and discordant band, seeking anything burnable that could be found. Water butts would be tipped over and trundled away, and an odd faggot or two picked up. On one never-to-be-forgotten occasion an attempt was made to remove an old wooden privy from a cottage garden. The attempt was only abandoned when someone suddenly discovered that it was occupied by an elderly lady full of righteous and burning indignation. However, in spite of an occasional setback they usually managed to get a fine blaze going before the night was out.

The village children, in spite of the low wages, were surprisingly well turned out as a rule, and if their mother had done well at pea- and potato-picking, the boys would be bought little corded suits with brass buttons and turned-down celluloid collars finished with red or blue ties, the outfit completed by black stockings over the knees and high lace boots. Boots, as always with a large family, must have been a problem, for they wore out rapidly on the rough gravel roads. The old beautifully pleated smocks worn by the old farm labourers were rarely seen in father's time, though he remembers seeing some of the men coming to church in them when he was very young. Farm workers' clothes are a minor miracle, now as then, and always seem to keep out the weather better than the ordinary person's mackintosh. Caught out in the rain, hedging perhaps, the

West Hanningfield Church

labourer puts a bag round his shoulders, and continues unperturbed with his work, and just doesn't appear to get wet. His trousers appear as seamed and marked and solid as his boots and, with a piece of string below each knee, they are as weathered as the land their wearers work on. A heavy coat with a poacher pocket and a cloth cap complete the outfit, though the amount of things that can be produced from the pockets of the average farm-worker handy-man has to be seen to be believed. Having been brought up with these men is probably why I have always remained singularly unimpressed by conjurors.

In those days the church pews were always full for both services on a Sunday, and the back pews, full of the village lads, were always under the close observation of the verger or beadle. The service was the only relaxation the people had from their normal hard-working lives, and they worshipped hard and enjoyed it. Besides which, they met their friends after church and compared notes on the week's work, their ailments, the weather, and the hundred and one things that went towards making the life of a country parish in those days. The whole parish was a closely knit unit which has been gradually disintegrating for the past fifty years or so.

For many years father contracted for carting the gravel with which the country lanes were kept repaired. The gravel was carted from nearby pits in Stock or Baddow, each cart usually making two journeys a day. The carters left the gravel along the middle of the stretch of road that was being repaired, and it was the roadman's job to come along and level it. This was another of the jobs for which an early morning start was made, and father, who sometimes took a cart himself, remembers driving into the pits on winter mornings with the moon still shining.

The one day's holiday in the year which all the horsemen and most of the day labourers took, was always on the occasion of the annual agricultural show. Dressed in their best black, they were usually lent the pony trap, and if the show were being held near at hand, drove there direct, or if not, into Chelmsford, and then on by train. As the show was usually a two-day affair the farm workers attended on the second day when the admission prices were lower. They always visited the tents of the firms which had dealings with their employers, and were given a free drink, and, when this happy duty had been done, would make a slow, critical, and highly enjoyable circuit of the exhibits. It was the custom with the Link House men always to have a meal in Chelmsford on the way home; sausages, bread, and tea, and if a man consumed less than three-quarters of a pound of sausages it was rather implied that he 'couldn't take it.' Nowadays, so much has interest died and other amusements taken its place, the agricultural show, though it is still successfully held every year, is only sparsely attended by farm workers.

Weddings and funerals do not, in their essentials, change from century to century, but they have lost one or two charming customs. At West Hanningfield in the old days, when the daughter of a farmer or other local notability was married, the school children would line the path carrying bunches of flowers. When the happy pair made their appearance, the children scattered the flowers in front of them as they walked down the path. The first time father's young sister Annie was allowed to be present at this ceremony she grew so excited waiting for the bride and groom to emerge that, when they finally did, instead of scattering her flowers she threw basket and all. This custom was still observed when my mother was married at West Hanningfield in 1909.

Sometimes when an old horseman who had served all his life on one farm died, his own pair of horses would draw him to church in the wagon with which he had made so many moonlight morning starts and drawn home so many harvests.

The school children usually had their couple of treats every year. Traditionally one was held in the village school at Christmas, and the other on the rectory lawn at hay-time. The first was notable for the usual decorations (especially long rows of many-coloured egg-shells), the distribution of an orange and a bag of sweets to every child, and, the *pièce de résistance*, magnificently rowdy musical chairs. The real core of all treats, however, is the tea, and there is a story which my mother's father, the Rev. Walter Wace, told, of a small boy at one Christmas treat. He was almost the last survivor, and was fighting a draw with a large sticky doughnut. Grandfather noticed he looked a bit green, and asked him solicitously how he felt.

'Not very well, sir,' was the reply, 'but I'll have to feel a good deal wuss afore I gives in!'

The second or summer treat was held on the shady rectory lawns and, after tea, the children went out to play in the hay on the rectory meadow. There were races and scrambling for sweets, and, when it rained, musical chairs and games in the coach house. Only the ubiquitous 'stop-me-and-buy-one' was absent from the happy scene.

For many years, through the kindness of some long-dead benefactor, large families and old people could obtain parish bread from the church all through the winter, and this was occasionally supplemented by a hundredweight of coal. At East Hanningfield the children's treats were supplemented every January by a mothers' and fathers' treat. The parents were entertained to tea and a concert, and each man on leaving was given a pipe and half an ounce of baccy.

When father first applied to Sam Tyler for permission to learn to plough, Sam, in company with his brother horsemen, said:

'You bring us some beer, and we 'll larn you to plough!'

Father dutifully obtained and brought the beer, and took turns driving the various teams up and down the field. When, after a week or so, his furrows were becoming less devious and conforming more to the regulation 'straight and narrow,' the teamsman would sit at the top of the field happily drinking father's 'bribe,' and critically watching his pupil. The only fault the horseman had to find with father was that he picked it up too quickly!

I was talking to an old cottage woman not long ago, and what she said is, I think, the best epitaph on what I have tried to describe as 'The Village Scene.'

'We were all so happy then,' she said.

JRPopham

CHAPTER VII

EARLY RESPONSIBILITY

WHEN grandfather died father was nineteen, and the full weight of running the farms fell on his shoulders, with his younger brother, Frank, to help him. The neighbours were very apt to criticize the two young men, which did not help to make their task any easier. August 1881 was a wet miserable month, and father, using four horses to get each load home, was told again and again he was carting his corn too wet. However, he left most of the stacks standing till spring, and the corn came out dry and plentifully, so all was well and the neighbours disproved.

Grandfather had been the vicar's warden at West Hanningfield, and, at the first church meeting held after his death, Mr. Kemball, the rector, proposed father to take his place. One of the neighbours, who all seemed determined to keep father down as much as possible, promptly jumped up and said he was under age, and therefore ineligible. Mr. Kemball spiked their guns by saying that in that case he would appoint no one till father was of age.

Father and Uncle Frank also made themselves unpopular by an excess of zeal in fattening a bunch of calves. They fed the calves so richly that the young animals got a form

of blood pressure, which affected their brains, causing them
to have continual fits. The vet was called in, and his
treatment consisted in piercing the dewlap or brisket with a
needle, which had a piece of tape attached. The tape was
pulled right through, and then the two ends tied together
under the dewlap. The tape, known as a 'seton,' maintained
an issue for discharges and acted as a counter-irritant. After
this had been done the calves wasted rapidly for a time, but
eventually began to put on flesh slowly and healthily, and
made good cattle after all. Grandmother, as father puts
it, was 'pretty waxy' on the subject of overfeeding for
some time after this.

At the same time as the calf incident foot-and-mouth
broke out again in a bunch of bullocks at Cannon Barns.
Father reported it to the police, but did nothing in the way
of treating the bullocks. They all recovered rapidly and
did well.

Beef was fetching good prices, and, accordingly, in the
following year, 1883, father planted thirty-two acres of
mangolds, thinking them good cheap food, as, of course,
they are. He learnt his lesson, however. Mangolds need
a lot of labour, chopping out, singling, and then keeping
the land as clean as possible. Afterwards he always grew
less than half this acreage, but put on the same amount of
dung as he had on the thirty-two acres. This produced
better results with far less labour. There is a story that
one year he had only two mangolds in the middle of a field,
but they were pushing each other into the ditch.

Only one day was lost that year during harvest, and the
barley ran so freely that grandmother objected to the heavy
threshing bill. Father told her she ought to be pleased,
not angry. He took a sample of barley that had been
grown in Long Marsh Field, and sold it to a Chelmsford
merchant for forty-one shillings per quarter. Afterwards
he found he had sold it too cheaply, and that the merchant

had done well out of it. He kept his own counsel and, later in the season, sold the same merchant another sample at a higher price. The market weakened a little, and the merchant, meeting father later, told him he had lost on the second lot all he had made on the first. It left them all square, and father felt that justice had been done.

Some of the neighbouring farmers still had grandmother's ear, and father, though always open to receive good advice, found their criticism maddening when he was doing his best and working as hard as he could.

On one day in the autumn of 1883, ten pairs of horses were out on the farms, drilling, mangold carting, and carting corn from the threshing machine. That autumn he planted a hundred and forty-three acres of wheat without an ounce of artificial manure, using only dung and, on some fields, soot. This latter was sown by old Cox at night, for which highly unpleasant job he was paid substantial overtime. Father still has great faith in soot, and would use it now if he could get hold of it.

The summer of 1884 was hot, with hay and roots scarce. At harvest time father bought his first 'Handy' reaper. This extraordinary machine had two seats, on one of which sat the driver, and on the other a man with a rake whose job it was to gather the corn into bundles as it fell on to the machine's platform. These bundles would then fall off, and be tied by men who stood waiting round the corn, each with his own stretch to keep tied up. One harvest father took this machine over to Cannon Barns, and cut eleven acres of wheat in one day, which was quite an effort. His gang that day included four women, two women taking the place of one man. The field was finished about half-past eight, and father, instead of being praised for his industry, was told off for being late for supper. And on the following morning he was accosted by four irate husbands who had been kept waiting for their supper the night before. He has always been careful to knock off in good time since that day.

This same machine caused a violent argument between father and Badeley, the landlord. It was September, and harvest was finished long before. Baddeley, who kept the shooting rights himself at that time, was out after partridge, and kept complaining bitterly and continually about the new Handy reaper. Not unnaturally the machine cut the corn much shorter and cleaner than the best reaper-gang, and therefore it left far less cover and food for the partridges. Father also had most of the hedges well down, and Mr. Badeley, a keen shot, became more and more irritable as the day went on. Near Partridge's Brook father's patience gave out.

'Look here, sir,' he said. 'You 've grumbled all day. I keep the farms as well as I can, and you won't worry me into my grave like some of whom I could tell. No, I 'm damned if you will!'

Mr. Badeley had little to say, owing, possibly, to the close proximity of the brook. Grandmother drove the point home by sending in her notice, for times were hard, and it was one way of getting the rent reduced, as it did in this case. For farmers were quitting in large numbers, and their farms were standing vacant. A tenant at a reduced rent was a good deal better than no tenant at all. Lord Petre was the largest landowner in the district, and to fill his empty farmsteads his agent advertised them in Scottish papers, and the influx of Scots farmers into East Anglia really began in earnest. The old village families were leaving the country and going into the towns, and many threshing machines, left without corn to thresh, were broken up and used for firewood.

However, in spite of these hard times, a hard core of farmers, who adapted themselves to the changed conditions and need for hard slogging work, kept going, and were continually reinforced by new Scots farmers, all of whom worked hard themselves, and did with far less labour than had been thought necessary before.

Crops were good in 1885, and huge stacks of wheat stood at Link House and about the fields, and most of them produced fifty to sixty quarters apiece, selling at thirty shillings per quarter.

Up to 1888, when traction engines first began to be used the threshing machines were driven by seven- or eight-horse-power portable steam engines. They were taken from farm to farm by the farmer who had last employed them, on to the next place where they were wanted, and so on. When father was busy he would pay four men a shilling apiece to shift the threshing tackle after their day's work. He remembers sending it off to Crabb's Farm one night in the spring of 1886. No one worried about un-lighted vehicles in those days, and machine and engine, with four horses apiece, clattered out of Link House yard on their five-mile journey to the other end of the parish just as the spring dusk began to fall. The horsemen were also given a pint of beer before they started, and another on their return. With wages at eleven to twelve shillings a week, an extra shilling and a couple of pints were not to be sneezed at.

The hay-time of 1886 saw father dealing with his first hot haystack. He always likes to get a bit of heat in his stacks, holding that hay is poor stuff when picked up so dry that it fails to heat at all. Therefore every three or four years we have a hot stack, and all sniff anxiously in the early morning when the smell is at its strongest, and plunge long irons into the centre of the stack. The state it has reached can be judged from the wisp of hay that comes out on the end of the iron. From time to time a stack heats up a little too much, and has to be turned right over, and that is what had to be done to the stack at Link House in 1886. It took all one day and till eleven o'clock the next, and father was so generous with beer for the men that they became quarrelsome. Father said it didn't matter, because they worked all the harder. Turning a stack is killing work with strong fumes coming off the hot hay, and in those days they had no elevator to carry the hay from the old stack to its new site. The smell of the hot hay gets into the men's boots and clothes, and stays there for days.

The night after his first stack turning father went to a vestry meeting at West Hanningfield, without changing his clothes. After the meeting had been going a few minutes another farmer who was present began to wrinkle up his nose and sniff. Presently he interrupted the meeting.

'Excuse me, sir, excuse me,' he said to Mr. Kemball, the rector, 'but if there isn't a hot haystack somewhere near here it's a wonder to me!'

He went to the window, and, opening it, hung out his head and sniffed again. Soon he had the whole meeting sniffing, and out on the church path. By then father thought the joke had gone far enough, and let it be known that the smell of hot hay was in his clothes and boots, and was not being wafted into the vestry on the evening breeze from some far-off stack.

The year 1887 saw improved conditions, and grandmother was able to put away a considerable sum out of the farm profits. The corn at Cannon Barns ran extraordinarily well. One big barley stack in particular was begun by the threshing gang while the moon still shone cold in the early dawn, and was only finished as dusk fell. It yielded eighty quarters, and as it was too dark to see to pay the men, father, the threshing gang, and the Cannon Barns men all adjourned to the 'Plough and Sail.' The little bar was full of tired dusty men, drinking their pints with the immense satisfaction of men who have a hard day's work behind them, the whole scene lit by a swaying oil lamp, and soon blue with the smoke from the shag in a score of clay pipes. This was on a Saturday night, and the following week the tackle came to Link House and, keeping up the good work, threshed one hundred and fifty quarters off two stacks. The last stacks of that harvest were not threshed till the following June.

Hay, too, was very plentiful, but cheap. Grandmother made father sell it, in spite of his violent protests that it would pay for keeping, and was bound to be worth more in a year or two. His protests were amply justified, for the next hay-time was wet and prices soared.

Queen Victoria's Jubilee was celebrated in 1887, and father remembers a dinner held in the meadow opposite the church, which the whole village attended. A boiling sun beat down on the heads of the villagers, but a day's holiday in those times, with a free meal thrown in, was something worth having, and no one grumbled at the lack of shade.

The bridge over the Can in London Road, Chelmsford, was washed away in 1888, and father says that incident typifies the year. Spring sowing was delayed till Easter Monday, and it was 1st September before a load of corn had been carted. Clover which had been planted in barley as its parent crop stood higher than the barley itself, so that the crop needed as much 'making' as hay. Father never says much about such bad years, just that he was 'glad to see the back of them.'

Another heavy hay crop in 1889 sent the Link House beer bill soaring to thirteen pounds for the season. Hay-making is hard work, and a few pints of beer do wonders. In those days father paid twenty-eight shillings a barrel, which worked out at about three-ha'pence a pint, and beer was beer then, as any of the old men will tell you. When, as rarely happens now, father and I go and have a pint in a public house, father downs it more or less in one gulp, and says, with an expression of sorrow: 'You could drink a gallon of it, and never know you 'd had a drop!'

He has no use for a man who takes more than two or three swigs at a pint.

'You 're like a chicken drinking out of a pan,' he says disgustedly.

Father has nothing to say of 1890 beyond that it was a bad year, with poor crops, but the next year he and Uncle Frank between them hired the Lodge Farm, East Hanningfield. Grandmother gave them six hundred pounds; by hard work and ingenuity and denying themselves most of the pleasures of this world they had saved a further five hundred pounds between them, and to complete their capital they borrowed another two hundred pounds from grandmother. Father continued to look after the Link House farms, and Uncle Frank went to the Lodge. At this time father was getting eight shillings a week pocket-money out of the farm, an incredible fact, and, what was more incredible, it went towards paying the weekly wage bill at the Lodge. The gods were kind that year, and a good corn crop helped to tide things along.

Another bad year was 1892, and father says they had to 'scrap and claw' to keep things going. A field of spring beans (always a doubtful crop) which they put in at the lodge was so bad that they set fire to it as it stood as the cheapest method of harvesting. There is a revealing little verse about spring beans which father often quotes:

> 'One pod on a stalk,
> One bean in a pod,
> Just the seed again, by God!'

On 21st March 1893 the wind tacked into the east, and there it stayed till the following November. The cloudless hot weather was only interrupted by occasional thunderstorms. In Pan and other meadows father only cut patches

c

of grass, the remainder being too short for the mower.   He
sighed for the stacks of hay so prodigally sold in earlier
years, and gave swedes to the horses to make up for the
lack of hay in the diet.   When harvest came the wheat crops
were good, but the barley, suffering from lack of the occasional showers which make such a difference to a sample,
was poor.

With the hay and root crops practically non-existent, there
was little for the men to do, and father and Uncle Frank
contracted for carrying pipes for a new water pipe-line
that was passing through Rettenden.   Their figure of
one shilling a load easily undercut their competitors, who
laughed at them for doing the job so cheaply.   However,
as father said when they drew their fifty-pound cheque at
the conclusion of the contract, it paid the men's wages, and
was something for them to do.

As the drought continued the water supplies at Cannon
Barns gave out, and water had to be carted round by road
from Link House, a distance of two miles, every day.
Summer passed into autumn, with day after day breaking
into clear skies and hot sun.   Feed grew short on the
pastures, and sheep at Salisbury Fair could be bought for
under one pound apiece.

There is a good story of a dealer who, having bought a
bunch of sheep at a west country fair for seventeen or
eighteen shillings, brought them back to Essex.   A neighbouring farmer, who was a bit of a stay-at-home, and
wanted a few sheep, came round to have a look at them.

After his inspection he said, rather rashly, to the dealer:
'Well, I suppose you gave about twenty-six shillings
for them.'

The dealer, like most of his profession, a man of quick
wits, replied immediately:

'Now, ain't that funny?   You've guessed it straight
away.   That's exactly what I did give for 'em, and you

can have 'em for a couple of bob a head profit because I'm short of feed.'

The farmer, flattered, fell for it, and bought the sheep, leaving the wily dealer with ten shillings a head profit. This is a pretty fair example of how careful a farmer has to be when buying stock.

Prices, which had been hanging on a low level for so long, tumbled down in 1894. Wheat was sold at eighteen shillings a quarter, winter beans at one pound, and first-class barley at twenty-four shillings, while a friend of father's bought maize at thirteen shillings. The unfortunate labourer found his wages cut down to eleven shillings a week again, though on the whole he was not too badly off. He was often given a hundredweight of coal, could cut all the wood he wanted from the farm hedges, and got plenty of beer from the farmhouse. Bread was fourpence a four-pound loaf, and pork sevenpence a pound. Still, with a large family it must have been a pretty close thing.

Father would send pigs to the Ivy House to be killed by the local publican, named Joe May, and for these he was paid four shillings a stone dead weight. This excluded the head and pluck, which were thrown in, and could, therefore, be sold again at a cheap rate. This custom persisted up to the beginning of the war in 1914, and there has never been anything to touch Mrs. May's ham since, though a pig was occasionally killed at Link House and parts of it sent up to her to be cured. I remember hearing the last pig that was killed at Link House die, and being told by the stockman that, if I was a naughty boy, they would put a ring through my nose and fatten me up for the pot. This remark, coming on top of those ghastly dying shrieks, shook me to such an extent that I retired weeping to the house for reassurance that this could not possibly happen to me.

Another of the bad years about which father has little to say was 1895; it is best described by the fact that the stacks in the Link House stack yard dropped from a dozen down to only three.

One morning in the spring of 1896 father, stripped to his shirt, was loading barley from one of the big black-timbered barns at Link House, when Uncle Frank came walking up the yard. He stood looking at father working for a little while, and then he said:

'You're working hard, and you're not getting much for it. Don't you think it's time there was a change in this business?'

Father stopped to wipe the sweat from his forehead, thought a minute, and then walked slowly back into the barn and put on his coat and waistcoat.

The tempo of the farm slowed down gradually and imperceptibly, and father, for the first and only time in his life, took things easily. After a few weeks grandmother began to notice the alteration and, after several protests, herself suggested the change for which father and Uncle Frank were working. The following Michaelmas, after a period of life at Link House which father describes as 'very stormy,' they took over the farms.

At first both grandmother and her sons agreed to have Hilliard of Chelmsford to value for both parties, but then grandmother went out somewhere to tea, and had seeds of distrust sown in her by the still ubiquitous neighbours. She seemed abstracted on her return, and then announced that she was going to have two farmers, whom we will call Mr. Smith and Mr. Brown, to look after her interests.

Father was justifiably angry. This last effort of the neighbours was a little too much, and he promptly countered by procuring the services of Offin & Rumsey, a very 'up-and-coming' firm from Rochford. Hilliard still remained as a sort of umpire or third party.

Mr. Offin was a first-class valuer, and knew his job from A to Z, and Mr. Hilliard was also undoubtedly on the side of the two hard-working young men. Mr. Smith and Mr. Brown spent a rather unhappy afternoon.

When the final figure, which the joint valuers had decided on, arrived a few days later, father and Uncle Frank were delighted, but grandmother was exceedingly angry. The figure for the six hundred and twenty-five acres, dung, tillages, etc., was one thousand and eight pounds, an extraordinarily low amount, though it must be said in extenuation that most of the implements were in bad repair and extremely ancient.

After a stormy meeting with grandmother, Uncle Frank retired to the Lodge, and father spent as much time as possible out of doors. It was like walking into the centre of a hurricane every time he went into the house. However, when the first fury of the storm had subsided, they borrowed sixteen hundred pounds at four per cent from her, and launched into business on their own.

CHAPTER VIII

DIVERSIONS

INFORMATION on the subject of father's amusements is hard to come by. His hours of ease he enjoys after days of hard work, but he likes a rest on Sundays, varied by a leisurely walk round the farms to see that everything is in order. If and when these hours have to be taken up in other ways by what his family considers amusement, he bears with them, but only really gets going again when he is back in the round of farm life. As with many farmers his whole work, recreation, and life is taken up by the land.

He is prepared to give me all the data I need on the weather, crops, prices, etc., during every year of his life, but when I try to pin him down to tell me about his lighter hours the well of information dries up.

Being the eldest son of a family which included five daughters, he was often pressed into service as escort to dances. This was a form of pleasure which father had little use for. His record was five dances in a winter, and he recounts this with a shake of the head, and an expression of extreme distaste. How he must have brightened up when the band played the last waltz!

Once or twice he drove some of his sisters to dances given

by a family at Wickham Bishops, a distance of roughly sixteen miles. These were marathon affairs, and started with a tremendous meal, followed by a sing-song, and, when the younger members of the party were dithering with impatience, the dancing eventually started.

The tradition which my grandfather upheld was that the dance must go on till the first glimmer of dawn began to come through the windows. Father, however, not being an addict, and thinking moreover of the day's work ahead, usually managed to make his departure before the small hours. In any case he said it was a great mistake to go on so long. As the daylight grew and the lamps paled and began to gutter, the romance of the night died. The women's faces looked drawn and tired, and their evening gowns tawdry in the cold hard light. As father put it, they looked 'proper crutes.' Going home after one of these dances at Wickham Bishops, father fell asleep and woke suddenly to see the gleam of moonlight on the river at Hatfield Peverel mill. He thought for a moment he was off the road, and about to drive himself and his sisters into the river, and he completed the journey shaken and wide-awake. As the trap drove into Link House yard the men were coming to work across the horse meadow. Father had an hour on the sofa and then joined them.

Another pastime, which only endured for a year or two, was sparrow catching. A sparrow club was formed, with its headquarters at the Compasses Inn, and all members were required to produce the heads of twelve sparrows once a month. For the first year all the members were as keen as mustard, and all kept up their quota. Every night the catchers were out round the buildings or stacks of one farm or another. A sparrow-net is nailed between the top halves of two long poles, and lifted up to the side of a stack or under the eaves of a cart lodge. The startled sparrows fly out, and a third member of the party, holding a bright light midway between the two pole-bearers, dazzles them, making them fly into the middle of the net. The bearers bring their two poles together, and the unfortunate sparrows are swiftly dispatched.

The club, after a successful year, had a dinner at the 'Compasses,' but the next hay-time found the members too busy to produce their quota, and by harvest the club was defunct. This was probably a very good thing, as our small birds are far more friends than foes to the farmer.

Father was only a young man when he first began to attend the tithe dinners at West and East Hanningfield, there being Link House land in both parishes. As he was young, strong, and full-blooded, the port he consumed resulted in fierce nose bleeding. He never went to a tithe dinner without a handkerchief in every pocket, and always put the cellar key handy for when he got home. At these dinners the farmer paid his tithe, and received a good meal in return. All of which made for a spirit of goodwill, and was a very sound idea. The Rev. Mr. Tiddeman, who left West Hanningfield in 1878, was the last parson in this parish to carry on this admirable custom, though Canon Sacre at East Hanningfield continued it for some years longer.

On one famous occasion at West Hanningfield rectory a rather rough diamond, whom we will call Mr. Jones, found the amenities of the rectory dining-room rather lacking. There were no spittoons. Dinner had been finished, and the room was blue with smoke. In a muffled voice Mr. Jones tried to attract the rector's attention.

'I say, sir!' Pause. 'I say, sir!' Pause. 'I SAY, SIR!'

Mr. Tiddeman, deep in conversation, at last heard the appeal. Turning courteously, he inquired:

'Yes, Mr. Jones, what can I do for you?'

'Please, sir, I want to spit!'

Faced with this unusual situation Mr. Tiddeman kept his head admirably.

J. K. Popham

The ' Compasses,' West Hanningfield

'Well, Mr. Jones,' he said, 'if you 'll just wait a moment I 'll fetch you the coal scuttle!'

Father was passionately fond of cricket, and played a few seasons for Rettenden, a neighbouring village. However, after grandfather died the farms were a great tie, and he could find little time for the all-day matches which a few prosperous farmers round Rettenden arranged. It cost money, too, with lunch to pay for, and a sing-song in the evening, but it was bad luck for a young man in his early twenties to have to give up his favourite game. A large acreage to farm, and a large family to provide for, leave little time for long, slow, happy cricket matches on lovely summer days.

The weddings of his five sisters, which occurred at irregular intervals, were great occasions. The village band, which played the music in church before the organ was installed, always attended, and a thoroughly good time was had by all. At these times, or whenever there was a party, the men always played quoits. A year or two ago we were down in Surrey on a visit, and happened to notice some men playing quoits behind an old inn. Father sniffed like an old war horse, and said it was a pity I had never tried it. Now there was a game!

The day before visitors were coming to Link House one of the men was sent out into the front meadow with two pails and instructions to saturate two small squares of grass with water from the horse pond. The squares, which were about eighteen feet apart, were then covered with sacking to keep them damp for the next day's game of quoits. It was essential to have the ground wet for the quoits to fall true, and not bounce.

After tea next day out would come the quoits and the gentlemen would adjourn to the meadow. The quoits, which now lie rusty and neglected in the granary, are about the size of a tea-plate, and have a notch for the forefinger on their underside. A hen's feather would be stuck in the centre of each square and each contestant given his quoits, then, standing side by side on one square, they would throw at the opposite feather, then change ends, and so on. Nearest to the feather to count. 'Game,' as far as father remembers, was ten, or as agreed. Father's great rival was old Mr. Sam Ratcliff, who could outclass him if the squares were reasonably close together, but usually lost if the man who had stepped out the pitch had long legs.

'I always saw we had a good eighteen feet,' says father, grinning.

For many years the whole family had a grand reunion at Link House on Boxing Day. Of his five sisters, Kate and Lil had married farmers, Sophie a threshing-machine proprietor, who also farmed, and Annie a timber importer. Alice was at home, and married later, after this happy custom had died out. The yard would be filled with the different family equipages. The men would all go rabbiting, the party consisting of perhaps father and his two brothers, Frank and Ted, and such of the five brothers-in-law as happened to be present. The bag on some Boxing Days amounted to as many as one hundred and twenty rabbits, and there is no record of anybody being shot by any one else, which says a lot for the steadiness of the party.

In later years, when father and my Uncle Frank were in partnership, the shooting rights and rabbiting were let to a syndicate headed by Percy Garon, of the well-known Southend catering firm of that name. Father was a very indifferent shot, and rarely accepted an invitation to join their party. On one occasion, however, they asked him to join them at lunch. It was a very good lunch indeed, and father did full justice to it, and washed it well down.

When every one had finished two bags full of live rabbits were produced, and father was handed a gun, the idea being that the rabbits would be turned down one by one, and that father would probably miss them one by one.

After hearty protest he found himself standing alone, gun in hand, as the gamekeeper prepared to loose the first rabbit. Out of the bag it shot, and raced away. Father took aim, and the rabbit turned that sudden somersault which means he is shot through the head. The same thing happened every time, and the laugh was on the syndicate. Father claims no credit for the exploit—it was just one of those rare and happy days when the rabbits really do 'look as big as sheep.' Or perhaps it was the lunch.

To be strictly accurate, one could hardly include attendance at sheep fairs under the heading of diversions, but I am certain that father enjoyed these as a form of recreation more than anything else he did off the farm. For many years he attended the fairs at Bridford, Salisbury, and Appleshaw, and other places. He rarely came home empty-handed, usually buying a bunch of a hundred to a hundred and fifty, sometimes breeding ewes, but more often lambs, hoggets, or tegs, to be kept for a while and then sold again in Essex markets.

The first fair he ever attended was at Bridford, and he was accompanied by an elderly farmer called Mr. Speakman. They arrived the evening before the fair, and Mr. Speakman promptly led the way to a cottage which stood facing the fair ground, and where he knew lodgings could be obtained. They had a good supper, but just as they went upstairs the lady of the house said she did hope 'Arry's snoring wouldn't disturb them. Mr. Speakman, veteran of many sheep fairs, said he was sure it wouldn't, and father never gave it a second thought. The two of them shared a large four-poster, and both were quickly asleep. 'Arry went to bed an hour later, and was also quickly asleep. Mr. Speakman and father awoke simultaneously, and slept no more. 'Arry was in the room below, and his snores were of gargantuan proportions. Mr. Speakman made some rather savage remark about neglected adenoids, and father said that there was one thing to be said for 'Arry. At least the snores had a tremendously regular rhythm.

Towards dawn father dozed, and when he was woken by Mr. Speakman 'Arry's snoring was blending with the bleating of thousands of sheep, like a hideous cacophonic symphony.

There were eighty thousand sheep at the fair that year. The flocks were driven on the field and penned at the first streak of daylight, having in many cases rested on the roadside through the night, with shepherds, drovers, and dogs in attendance.

Probably owing to his first horrid experience with 'Arry, father rarely stayed the night at a fair again. Leaving Link House soon after midnight he would catch the two-thirty a.m. mail train from Chelmsford, and still arrive at whatever fair he was bound for in good time. On one occasion he visited the fair at Craven Arms, on the borders of Wales, with his brother-in-law, Percy Jackson. They bought a good-sized bunch of sheep, but then found there was no hope of getting them entrained till the morning. With the help of a rather decrepit drover, father and Percy Jackson made a fold for their flock on the fair field, and went to find beds for the night.

In the morning father went to see the auctioneer, who had guaranteed transport for all sheep bought at the fair. Father pointed out the additional expense and inconvenience caused by having to wait until the morning, and the auctioneer handsomely gave father a florin. This rendered father completely speechless, and it was left to the decrepit drover to comment:

'I 'd have chucked it back in the mean old ——'s face, sir. That I would!'

Apart from three or four short motoring trips during the

last ten years, father has but rarely been on holiday. In 1906, after his sister Lilian had died, he accompanied her husband, the same Percy Jackson, on a sea trip round England. They left Tower Bridge on a Saturday night, sailed round the west coast to Belfast, and then up to Glasgow; by rail to the east coast of Scotland, and then by ship again down the North Sea. The weather was bad, and father and the captain were the only people down for breakfast one morning, but out of the goodness of his heart father took a plate of porridge to Percy Jackson, who was lying miserably in his bunk. What Uncle Percy said to father has no place in this narrative. I can imagine father being horribly hearty. How he would have enjoyed being a sailor if he had been born in a seaport instead of on a farm!

My mother once managed to get him to Paris for a week, and this achievement must surely rank among minor modern miracles. On the morning they left, the farm seemed loath to let father go. A man at 'Frenches,' another small off-hand farm father rented at this time, broke his arm before breakfast; and then while he was snatching a hurried meal, a horseman came to the door with the news that one of the best horses was down with colic. However, mother got him into the trap, and they drove to Chelmsford station in an atmosphere of predestined doom. This was almost justified outside Victoria station. Father slipped on a piece of orange skin, and went down for the count. Mother says all hope left her as she looked at father lying there and a small crowd began to gather. However, father was unhurt, and must have only been meditating on the extreme foolishness of going for holidays.

Mother remembers that they lost their carriage rug on the train, and that both crossings were extremely rough, to her discomfort and father's huge joy. In spite of everything, the week was a great success, and they both thoroughly enjoyed themselves. Father's lack of command of the

French language worried him rather. He felt he was altogether too much in mother's hands. He made no attempt to master the intricacies of French coinage, which is maybe why mother enjoyed the holiday so much. It was the only time she ever had the free run of his pockets.

During the various expeditions they made by horse bus to places of interest, such as Fontainebleau, father always sat in front beside the driver, with whom he carried on an animated, if incomprehensible, conversation. The bus horses made common ground between them.

The first thing father saw when he looked out of the window after their first night in France was a little cart drawn by a dog. He was greatly interested in this, but never attempted to introduce it as a form of transport at West Hanningfield.

The thing that shook him most was when, after a meal of what he took for a tender spring chicken, mother told him he'd been eating frog. It must have been a relief to get home again and have a plate of good English beef in front of him, without the chance of its turning out to be something entirely different. Father took a very poor view of the frog incident.

CHAPTER IX

'HE CAN TURN HIS HAND TO ANYTHING'

'I RECKON that's got me beat,' says Tom Bell. 'I don't see how that can be done. No, I don't.'

Standing by talking to Tom about some job that needs doing on the farm one sees a first gleam of hope. If Tom says it can't be done it means that he's fast making up his mind about how he's going to do it. There may still be long discouraging preliminaries while he thinks it over, but only a stranger would be disheartened by these. The rest of us stand and wait. 'You'll see, owd Tom 'ull do that!'

Tom is but an example of that vast legion of farm workers which, in days of peace, was unappreciated for its true worth and was even a source of mirth to the townsmen. Working for a miserably small wage compared with that paid to the factory worker, while his sons drifted to the towns, he still toiled on. His daily pride and pleasure is in his work. To call him a 'jack of all trades' is to slander him grossly. There are no agricultural guilds, but if there were he would rank as master of his craft. He can be found on almost every farm. Someone is bound to say when asked a question:

'I don't know, but you ask owd Tom, he kin lay his hand to 'most anything.'

He may perhaps at one time have been a full-time horse-man or stockman, and, in the days before tractors, driven his pair of horses week in and week out, 'setting out' his fields, that is, striking the first furrows at regular intervals and according to plan, so that the stetches may have an equal number of furrows and the field be evenly divided for the drill and cultivation, then laying his furrows upright and even and utterly straight, sometimes 'havin' a goo' at a ploughing match and carrying off a prize or two, his horses always in the pink of condition, beribboned, with brasses shining, with only the sale ring or time to break up a beloved pair in which he had taken such pride.

Then came the advent of the tractor, when the internal combustion engine drew Tom like a magnet. Its subtleties and idiosyncrasies were there to be mastered.

'Do that 'll pull three furrows instead o' one, and look how much faster that do fare to git over the ground!'

He left his stable, not without regret, but perhaps his pair had been broken up and he was hardly used to his 'new uns.' In any case he never lost his deep affection for horses.

When the land is ploughed from harvest, the winter corn must be drilled, and Tom is always in charge of the drill. He produces a small bethumbed note-book from an inner pocket, in which he has jotted down from year to year the necessary adjustments which must be made to the drill for planting different crops. For some must go in in larger quantities than others, and many adjustments must be made.

'I'll have to change that barrel and put a bigger wheel on ready for the mornin',' says Tom to the 'guv'nor,' one night in late October. The barn floor is swept clean and they are busy 'wetting' the wheat with a copper sulphate preparation mixed with water, spreading the wheat out thin upon the floor, pouring on the mixture, then turning and re-turning till all the kernels are damped.

In the morning the clink of the coulters on the old Smythe drill comes clear across the misty fields, one man, Tom perhaps, walking on the steerage driving the horse and the other behind seeing that the corn runs evenly from the 'box' or hopper, that none of the coulters are blocked with earth, or, if the land is steep, tilting the box so that the corn still runs level. At each end of the field the men change places as the drill turns, and away they go again, stopping only to fill the box from the bags that lie along the hedge. The headlands have been drilled first, so that no land may be missed in the turning. For the drill-man's mistakes must confront him a long time, and be a constant source of leg-pulling by his mates. A blocked coulter may mean a row missed right up the field, and when the corn begins to spring it shows up and everybody notices it.

'I rec'lect once,' says Tom with a shudder, 'as how I once missed a whole stetch. Lord, I think I heard 'bout that when the corn came up. Still, that larnt me, that larnt me!'

Good drill work has little said about it, but bad, irregular, crooked work, or even perhaps only a slight deviation by a good man, soon causes comment.

'I see they drilled Ten Acres in figures of eight this year then?'

When the corn is drilled and harrowed in, the water furrows must be ploughed. These are single furrows ploughed along the natural water-courses of the field to let the water off the land. When ploughed the bottom must be levelled with a spade, and the turned furrow must be broken up into small pieces and thrown about so as not to impede the growth of young corn.

The skilled man gets over this work very quickly, and leaves the field satisfyingly neat and finished. Others never seem to get on with it.

'He 'll be on that field a week,' his mates say, looking over the hedge.

Soon now the threshing gang will come and, when they have gone, and the barn is filled with the threshed corn, Tom will be busy dressing a lot of barley for sale. Hour after hour the old wind dresser drones on, one man turning the handle, another putting the corn into the hopper, and the third shovelling away the dressed corn. Out from the back of the machine fly the weed seeds, small corn, and dust—above all, dust! Occasionally one of the men sneezes, and the cobwebs away up in the rafters gradually assume fantastic solid shapes as the dust settles heavily upon them.

The last sack goes through. The machine is lifted and moved. The waste is swept up and the sacking up of the corn begins.

'Do you keep that swept up clean,' says Tom. 'We don't want that all over the floor and us a-treadin' in it.'

'I reckon owd Tom 'ull want a rake and broom in his coffin, else he 'oont know what to do with hisself when he gits to heaven!' grins one of his mates.

The 'guv'nor' comes into the barn to speak to Tom.

'We 've got a bunch of bullocks coming into the yard to-morrow, Tom. Can you mend the mangers? Some of them have got the sides knocked out and the bottoms broken.'

Tom looks doubtful. 'Let 's go and have a look,' he says.

After inspection and consideration he gives his verdict:

'Do you let me have Bob to lend a hand, and fetch me the timber fust thing, I reckon I can have them fixed up for yer time you 're ready to turn they cattle in.'

And so, in the morning, the bullock yard is echoing to sawing and hammering, old broken wood is knocked out, old nails are carefully collected, and in the afternoon the mangers are ready. As good a job as any full-time carpenter would have done.

It is Tom, usually with Bob to help him, who replaces the broken or rotten gate-posts, hangs the new gates or repairs them, puts up any new fences on the farm, or post and rails to close the gaps.

'There,' he says, stepping back to look at his finished work, 'I'll reckin' that'll stop 'em!'

When there is time for a day's rabbiting it is usually Tom who goes with the 'guv'nor.' Fortunate indeed is the rabbit who escapes his gun. The farther away they are the better he likes them.

'You'll strain that old gun, Tom,' someone says when a particularly long shot comes off.

His nets are well set. Choosing the much-used run among the grass and bushes on the bank, he sets one carefully, probably some distance from the warren, so that the bolted rabbit, gathering speed, will blunder headlong into it. In a good earth perhaps five or six successive rabbits may fall a victim to this trap. Tom always has a good dog who, if the rabbits miss the net, will most likely catch them farther on down the ditch; or, lying flat on his belly close to one of the holes, snatch one neatly before it knows what is happening.

When the inevitable 'lay-up' occurs, and the ferret, with the rabbit up some deep dead-end, proceeds to the kill, Tom gets to work quickly. Once the line ferret is in and the line has stopped running, showing that the rabbit and loose ferret have been found, he starts to dig. From what seems instinct and years of long practice he will again and again dig straight down on the rabbit.

Not for him the amateur's hopeless 'Oh, we'll never get it out. We'll just have to wait for the ferret.'

Digging through roots and stones he goes until, throwing himself flat, he thrusts his arm into the hole. Farther and farther he shoves his arm, his face a study of intense concentration. Then, triumphantly:

'I got hold o' suthin'.'

Another long pause; then out comes his hand with the rabbit struggling violently in a last effort to escape or, if the ferrets have done their work, stiff and bloody.

Again, if the lay-up is in a place impossible for digging, under an old tree stump perhaps, he uses a long blackberry thorn. Divested of all branches and shoots, and with a carefully trimmed handhold, he inserts it up the hole till the thorns catch in the rabbit's wool. Then, turning steadily, he waits till the thorns have a good hold. Lastly, a long slow withdrawing of the thorn with the rabbit on the end. Naturally this can only be done on rare occasions, for the hole must be dead straight.

When a ton or two of hay wants cutting out of the stack for the horses and cattle Tom will make as good a job of it as the regular hay cutter. An inexperienced man will leave the side of the stack with jagged edges and long irregular slices like a poor carver with a joint, but Tom leaves the side of the stack as smooth as cheese cut with wire in a grocer's shop. The hay-knife, shaped like a swollen Turkish scimitar, with its short handle at a left-handed right angle to the blade, needs a great deal of practice and skill for efficient use. The blade must be kept upright against the stack, and each stroke must be regular and at the same angle as the last. Otherwise someone passing up the stackyard is sure to pause and gaze for a minute. Then:

'Someone's been a-gnawin' at that owd stack, I reckon,' comes the caustic comment.

Tom, asked to demonstrate, shows the questioner carefully.

'But that's mostly knack,' he says.

Tom can do his bit of hedging and ditching as well as the next man. With his bill and axe sharpened to their finest cutting edge he attacks the high old hedge fiercely. Soon the faggots of wood lie neatly bundled, bound by withies. The oak, ash, and thorn stubs stand along the bank like hulks of octopuses shorn of their limbs.

Underfoot the carpet of old small leaves deadens the footfall. The animal haunts are laid bare to every passing eye, and higher up the field a great fire of waste wood and undergrowth flares and crackles in the winter afternoon. Tom may be laying on a hedge of thorn bushes as he goes along, or if the hedge is to be removed in order to throw two fields in together only the stubs are left. These may be dug up later, or blown out, or alternatively pulled out by steam engine.

It is likely, too, that when the hedge is down Tom will be cleaning out the ditch so that the land lies dry and the drains run freely. Each spadeful of earth goes on the land side of the ditch, and not on the hedge bank, for from there it would slide back into the ditch in time.

Tom's bent shoulders and head move just above the level of the ditch. His boots are ankle deep in mud and water.

'Are your feet wet, Tom? Why don't you put your rubbers on?' you ask.

Tom shakes his head.

'No, no, I don't want no rubbers for diggin'. These owd boots 'oont let the water in.'

He pulls one heavy wrinkled boot from the water.

'My feet are as dry as a bone,' he says proudly.

As the days lengthen with spring Tom never misses an evening in his garden. Passing down the road perhaps one may hear him in conversation with Bob his neighbour.

'I reckon you beat me for spring cabbage this year, Tom,' Bob says. 'They "Flower o' Spring" did wonderful well.'

'Yes, I had they plants from owd Brown up the forge,'

Tom replies. 'He mostly gets a good stock. Still you mostly beat me for onions and carrots. How're you off for runner-bean seed?'

Leave them talking in the soft spring dusk and leave their gardens, the old flower shows, or the church at harvest festival to show their prowess.

Soon now the spring corn must go in, followed by the root crops, and all the land should have its dressing of fertilizer. Many farmers use mechanical distributors, but large numbers still employ their men on broadcasting. The bags of artificial manure are laid across the fields in rows, and each man carries a large wooden basket or 'cob,' which he fills and refills as he passes each row of bags.

With his cob slung on his right arm he walks slowly up and down the field. At every other step his left hand goes into the cob, and the fertilizer flies out in front of him like a plume of breaking spray. On each journey an equal width of ground must be covered and the manure fall evenly, or here again the crop will tell the tale with an uneven growth.

Tom shakes his head about this job on a windy day.

'That ain't no sense,' he says. 'I see Allen's chaps a-broadcastin' yesterday. That wind was blowin' the stuff right across his field, over the road, and into our Five Acre. Reckon that ought to grow suthin' next year.'

For a day or so, till the rain washes it away, the road hedge is grey as though dirty driven snow had covered it.

As soon as the young beet and mangold are big enough to see, the chopping out and singling must begin. If possible, extra labour is obtained, but usually Tom and his mates have to give a hand to get the job finished. A back-breaking task with each row seeming to stretch into infinity, and the movement of each man hardly noticeable, yet Tom's hoe keeps on its steady pull and shove, and soon the thin straggly line of plants, nine inches to a foot apart, is stretching out behind him. The new man meanwhile is working his heart out twice as hard behind, bending to single each plant with his fingers and wondering how the hell Tom makes it look so easy.

Round about the end of May there are the ewes to be shorn. Heavy and bulky in their fleeces they lie panting under the hedges on hot days.

'We'll have those ewes out to-morrow, Tom,' is the 'guv'nor's' good-night order.

In the morning Tom puts on the old clothes he keeps specially for shearing and looks at the sky. The first bunch of ewes have been picked out the night before, because the fleece must be dry for shearing and, even without rain in the night, a heavy morning dew will delay the start some hours. The night has been made horrid by these ewes and their temporarily bereaved lambs. Grouped round the meadow gate the lambs make continuous and bitter complaint.

The machine is a hand-driven clipper, and Tom has George to turn for him. The wooden shearing platform is laid across the yard, and each sheep is lifted on so that the fleece may be kept free from dung and straw. The first ewe is caught and Tom dumps it between his knees on its backside. He opens the wool down the neck with his hands, and then, taking the clipper, starts work. From the centre of the neck he cuts round to the spine, and on right down the left-hand side of the sheep. Then, twisting the sheep on its axis, he cuts from spine to neck again. The fleece falls away in front of the clipper, a rich creamy blanket. Some sheep have an almost bare stomach, while in others it is thickly wooled. This may be cut any time when the sheep lies handy for it.

'Here's an easy one.' Tom grins as he turns up a bare belly. 'You hairy owd sheep,' he remarks to one more liberally covered.

This attempted description of shearing is, of course, just the rough theory. It is interspersed with violent struggles and kicking, while the fleece entwines round the sheep's hind legs, and the general effect makes an all-in wrestling match look like a quarrel in a kindergarten.

Tom always takes the most heavily fleeced first, leaving any scantily covered ewes till the end of the day.

'I like the wust fust,' he declares. 'I can work them others when I'm gettin' tired.'

One by one the shorn ewes leave the platform, smooth and glistening pink. As the day gets warmer the grease in the fleece begins to run, and Tom can make a better job of each sheep and work faster. Gradually the wool sheet, slung up by ropes on beams alongside the platform, begins to fill with the rolled fleeces. The sides bulge and George gets in to tread the fleeces down.

After midday the first bunch is turned out, and their lambs run in fright from these strange white apparitions. Their own hunger and their mothers' familiar voices soon convince them that all is well, however, and soon their tails are waggling ecstatically in a glorious overdue feed.

Tom doesn't wait to watch them discover each other.

'They'll soon find one another out. Let's get on with the others.'

The ewes are never all shut up at once, for this would mean too long a parting for some families. Painful for the ewe's udder and bad for the lamb.

The whirr of the machine goes on. The beer bottles are nearly all empty now, and dusk is slowly dimming the light in the yard.

'Moost time we packed up, Tom, isn't it?' asks George, whose arm has been aching badly these last few hours.

Tom finishes his sheep before replying. Up it gets, its back as smooth as silk, not an uneven ridge to be seen. Tom looks at it approvingly.

'Reckon we shall have to leave these laſt few till mornin'. That's a pity. They cut well now,' he replies.

He ſtraightens his back painfully and luxuriously.

'That's wuth a sovereign,' he says.

One lovely June morning out comes the grass-mower from the cart lodge, covered with duſt, and perhaps a winter's sparrows' droppings in the seat. Carefully Tom goes over it to see if all is well, the knives are sharpened, the horses hitched on to the pole, and soon the sound of the diſtant mower is an integral part of the murmur of the summer day. While the horseman drives, Tom is busy knocking nails into the top bar of the meadow gate, so that he can easily wedge the spare knife for sharpening. For it may take him half an hour, and:

'You may as well do it comfortable,' says Tom, ſtarting to work with his rub.

In a few days, with good weather, the rake will be on the go, and the hay gathered in long rake rows across the field. Then, one man to each row, the cocking begins. Several of the men merely roll three or four of the wads left by the rake together, round up the heap, and move on. But not Tom. Each wad muſt be moved and piled carefully, the bottom pulled out evenly with the fork, and the cock topped up to keep out the rain. With all his extra trouble he ſtill keeps up with everybody.

'Make yer cocks small,' he admonishes some newcomer, 'they 'll make all the quicker.'

When the field is fit to cart Tom is on the ſtack, and two or three of the old tried hands loading the wagons. Loading is not as easy as it looks, and is done on a definite plan, backwards and forwards in layers along the length of the wagon. Otherwise, when it comes to unloading the wagon it is wickedly hard work, with the man ſtraining his guts out trying to pull out hay which won't come off because he hasn't moved the bit which lies next to it, and on which perhaps he is standing. The middle of the wagon must be kept full, or the loader stands in a hole with the hay mounting round him and feeling like someone caught in a quicksand; but never too full, or the sides may slip out.

There is one important point for the man pitching the hay to remember. If he puts a forkful of hay over the front or back, the loader may claim half a gallon of beer. This is because it may disturb the corners of the load, and it may be difficult for the loader to get hold of. A good pitcher watches his loader, and puts the hay as near as possible where the loader wants it.

What is true of loading may also be applied to the stack itself. Tom, treading round and round the edges of the rising stack, reminds his mate again and again:

'Keep yer middle full, George. You must keep the middle full if you want to keep the water out.'

There's no one like Tom for looking after a gang of pea-pickers. He combines the diplomacy of an ambassador with the persuasive powers of a tipster. He keeps the women, children, and the travelling pea-picking professionals, each in his or her own stetch, sees that the haulm is picked clean, and knows to an ounce if each bag has the required forty pounds in it.

'No, no, missus, that bag don't weigh no more than thirty-five pounds,' he tells one good lady who is in a hurry to finish her day's work. She forcibly contradicts him, but Tom moves on unperturbed, returning only when he considers she has had ample time to make up the required weight.

'Some on 'em want a bit of watching,' is his remark at the end of the day.

The winter oats are changing colour now, and harvest is nearly here. Tom gets out his scythe and sharpens it up ready for cutting round the first field, to let the tractor and binder in. Later on the cutting round will probably be done with the horse-binder to save time, but as yet times are not too busy, and Tom, who likes to see things done properly, suggests 'we make a job of it and cut round.'

Steadily he swings his scythe round the field, long steady strokes, leaving the stubble as even as a board. It looks easy to the onlooker, who asks to have a go, but soon he finds that the point of the scythe sticks suddenly in the ground. Looking behind him he sees the stubble looking like a badly shaved chin.

Tom is tolerant.

'You learn to sharp yer tool well and practise a bit, that 'll soon come to yer.'

Then, suddenly, harvest is in full swing. The tractor roars all day in field after field. The almost inevitable breakdown finds Tom and his mate, covered with dust and grease, on their backs under the tractor.

'Here 's the trouble,' says Tom, producing a broken casting. 'Do you slip and get that for us as quick as you can, we 'll soon be on the goo agin.'

The cutting soon gets ahead of the men traving, and after a time it must be stopped so that all hands can get the corn stood up. It is essential to trave with care, otherwise, as Tom says:

'You 're only a-makin' work for yerself.'

If the weather is bad heavy rain or wind will blow down two out of three carelessly built traves, and these must be built up again to dry.

Tom bumps the bottom of his first sheaf hard into the ground, and then divides the head with his hands so that his mate's sheaf folds closely into it; then two sheaves on one side of the centre pair; then two on the other, so that the weight is evenly divided.

In a few days the wagons are creaking across the fields, and Tom is putting up his stacks in the stack yard or by field gateways. Broadening out from their bottoms they rise

and then draw sharply in to a steeply shelving roof.   Again
he reiterates his maxim:

'You must keep yer middle full.   Specially when you top
up.   If you get a good steep roof and the bottoms of your
sheaves are all tilted down, the stack's half thatched itself.'

Hardly is the last load home before the thatching must
begin.

'That ain't no sense gettin' yer corn home dry and then
let it stand and get wet,' Tom grunts as he lifts the ladder
up against the first stack.

Tom is no fancy thatcher.   He leaves no weather vanes
at his gable ends, but he keeps the corn dry, and his work
is pegged down against the strongest autumn gale.

These few of Tom's jobs only scratch at the surface of
what he can and does 'lay his hand to,' but they may
serve to show the reliability of him and his kind, and
perhaps give them some of the appreciation they deserve.

As the autumn dusk falls Tom goes home from covering
the last stack.   The farming year has completed its cycle.

'I reckon that land'll plough well termorrer,' Tom
thinks as he goes indoors.

Outside a great barn owl sweeps round the dim shapes
of the finished stacks in search of an early mouse.

CHAPTER X

PARTNERSHIP

WEST HANNINGFIELD, owing to a disagreement among
the farmers, failed to observe Queen Victoria's Diamond
Jubilee in June 1897 by any form of celebration or thanks-
giving, and for this the next day they got their just deserts
—though many of the innocent villages who had celebrated
most loyally suffered even more severely. About ten
minutes to three in the afternoon the sky darkened suddenly, and without any further warning a violent hailstorm
swept across a narrow strip of country. West Hanningfield
was not in the centre of its path, but, as it was, suffered
severely enough. The wind was from the west, and the
hailstones, nearly as big as walnuts, smashed all the windows
on the west side of Link House, and broke the glass in the
little greenhouse to smithereens. Chickens were killed as
they ran for shelter, and fields of corn, just coming out in
ear, were flattened out like a billiard table. In twenty
minutes the storm had passed on, leaving, as the Sunday
papers say, 'devastation in its wake.' A public fund was
opened to aid the farmers through the year, and a few,
whose crops had been light anyway, did quite well out of

it. The people who really felt the draught were the threshing gangs, for the corn sheaves had no ears left on them, and were nothing but bulky bundles of tangled straw.

In January 1898 the Rev. Mr. Tiddeman died, and his place was taken a few months later by the Rev. Walter Wace, one of whose daughters was to marry my father some thirteen years later. This year is also a vintage one in father's memory.

One hot day in early May father and Uncle Frank with one man to help them caught and washed four hundred sheep in the little lane that ran along the side of Link House pond.

'Of course,' father says, 'we drank plenty of beer or we should never have done it.'

He felt tired and sore and stiff for a week, and it was the last time he washed sheep before shearing. The wool, when washed, was worth a little more, but not enough to make the labour of washing worth while. The shearers grumbled for a year or two when they found a sheep with a particularly dirty fleece, but they soon got used to it.

'This one ain't never seen no water,' they said.

In those days it was possible to buy a bunch of sheep, shear them, and sell them again, and have a small margin of profit. This became impossible, though it was only some nine or ten years ago, when wool prices reached new low levels, that father finally stopped buying his spring bunch.

That harvest father used his first modern-type binder at Link House, and had good crops to cut with it. When the cutting was finished and carting about to begin, one of the horsemen went sick, and father, taking his place, had a month's carting straight off with the harvest gang. Five wheat stacks stood along the top of Road Field at Cannon Barns, and it took the threshing tackle five days to thresh them. Wheat prices were very low, and father sold the corn from these stacks at twenty-two shillings per quarter, though he had to weigh his sacks up to nineteen instead of eighteen stone apiece to get as much as this. Threshing cost about one shilling and tenpence per quarter for wheat and barley then, as compared with five shillings per quarter to-day, and oats were threshed at one and sixpence compared with four and sixpence.

When father reappeared at market after his month's sojourn in the harvest field, one of the merchants happened to notice his hands. Holding one of father's hands, palm outwards, between his, he called to his friends.

'Come and look here,' he said. 'Old John 's been busy. His palms are as corny as a crab's back.'

The thatching bill that year was large, with three hundred and sixty-five square feet to be paid for, one hundred square feet equalling one thatching 'square.' Thatching prices have not increased as much as most things since those days. Hay was thatched for one shilling per square, and corn for one shilling and twopence. Nowadays the allowed price is about two shillings and sixpence to three shillings.

One Thursday evening the following November a middle-aged man called in at the 'Plough and Sail,' and sat there most of the evening drinking beer. Near by in Pan Meadow was a bunch of twelve bullocks father had bought a few days before. During the evening the stranger remarked on the good quality of the cattle, and then, as the last customer left, he bade the landlord good night and, picking up his stick, a drover's cane, he walked off up the road in the opposite direction to Pan Meadow.

Early next morning father was called with the message that one of the men was at the back door and wanted to see him quick.

'They bullocks are gone from Pan Meadow, master,' was the remark that greeted father when he reached the back door. Father lost no time and, like the kings of ancient history, sent forth couriers north, south, east, and west.

Within an hour or so news reached him that the cattle, with the stranger from the 'Plough and Sail' in attendance, were only a couple of miles or so north-west of Link House, near a farm called Tanfield Tye. The 'gentle stranger' had driven them out of Pan Meadow during the small hours, right past Link House, and through West Hanningfield, without attracting any attention. He might have got away very nicely with the whole affair, but he must have suffered from an o'erweening ambition, and at the far end of the village, near the old 'Plough' public house, he turned the bunch sharp right down the road towards Tanfield Tye. He had noticed another bunch of cattle in a field near the Tye, and now resolved to amalgamate the two bunches, acting perhaps on the adage that 'he might as well be hung for a score as for a dozen.' Any one who has had any experience of droving will know that trying to amalgamate two bunches of cattle during the hours of darkness and by yourself is apt to be a disastrous experiment, as this proved. When father's courier arrived the cattle were spread over several fields, or running, tails up, headlong down the road. The 'rustler,' with day breaking and a sight of the distant courier, gave up the unequal struggle, and disappeared hurriedly across country. Some distant market was the poorer by a keen middle-aged dealer with a couple of bunches of strong young cattle to sell cheap.

Some months later the same gentleman, whose activities were surely more suited to Dead-Man's Gulch than West Hanningfield, slipped up badly when removing some sheep from another farm, and was caught. In any case he seems a neglected figure in contemporary 'blood-and-thunder' fiction.

Another exceptional year was 1899, and saw the century out with good crops, and a good trade for sheep and bullocks. Father and Uncle Frank paid off one thousand pounds of their borrowed capital.

D

'But,' says father, 'by God, we worked!'

The new century started with a cycle of bad years, and during the scanty 1900 harvest a friend of father's named Tom Blyth said philosophically:

'Well, perhaps the last years the harvests have been almost too heavy to deal with!'

Father regarded this remark as almost blasphemous, and Tom Blyth never said anything about over-heavy crops again, as wet harvest succeeded wet harvest in dismal succession.

Early in 1901 the weather taught father one of the many lessons he has learned from it. For a week or more it was fine and warm, but it was early for spring sowing, and father held his hand, waiting for the land to dry out a bit more. However, the fine spell broke suddenly, and it was April before it was possible to get on the land again.

'Never no more do I wait for the weather,' said father then, and though he still hangs on a day or so longer than other people, he rarely misses an opportunity to beat the weather.

The wet spring was followed by a showery summer, and when the land finally dried out in October it was iron hard. The horsemen got so sick of ploughing the concrete-like ground that they told father they wished he'd get sick of buying the shares that wore out at such an incredible rate.

The year 1902 proved to be the third successive wet year. Another bad harvest, with barley lying so long in the trave that it was of poor quality and worth little. Wheat and oats showed plenty of straw, but there was little corn in it. It was yet another harvest when the wagons creaked slowly home, cutting deep ruts in the field.

The weather decided to give the farmers a break after harvest, and they made the most of the opportunity to get a plant of corn. This clemency was only short-lived, however, and father found himself unable to cut several

meadows at next hay-time. Other farmers' haycocks came
floating down Partridge's Brook and, the brook suddenly
subsiding, lay in huge heaps in the river meadows till
Christmas, when father had them burned.

This delightful summer was followed by a harvest so
wet that the new binders could not be used. This meant
a revival of the old-time reaping harvests, and the old hands
came back into their own again for a brief space. Father
helped mow, and, as he crossed the water furrows, the
water stood deep and brown from the heavy rains.

The thing father remembers most distinctly about 1903
is how stiff he felt the morning after his first day's mowing.
He could hardly move in his bed, and thought bitterly of
happier harvests driving the binder with a team of good
horses in front of him.

After this wet hay-time and harvest father had taken a
brief holiday at Llandudno in the following May. Arriving
in Llandudno on Saturday night he spent his usual uneasy
time while on holiday, and left early on Tuesday morning.
Reaching London he took a fast train to Colchester, and
bought a hundred sheep at a sale. He then went home with
a satisfying feeling of having quickly made up for the lost
time.

Yet another in the dismal succession of wet harvests was
1904. Father had tried growing some bearded spring
wheat, and was rewarded by a crop that produced one
quarter per acre on one Cannon Barns field.

Mole-draining began to replace the old laborious land-
ditching, and father had several fields 'moled' with good
results. It was still necessary to dig the 'leads' from the
end of the mole-drain into the ditch, and father always had
the same two men on this job. He wondered for some
time why it was that one drain would run freely and well
into its ditch, while the next hardly ran at all. He began to
watch his lead-diggers, and one day caught one of them

putting in the lead drain before he dug down deep enough to reach the mole. From what I've heard of father that afternoon from other sources it must have been one of the few times in his life when he was really angry. However, with the moling costing only ten shillings per acre, father found it more than paid for itself in one year's crop.

The same steam tackle that did this draining for father also did a great deal of ploughing for him. It was held together by an elderly man who drove the ploughs, cultivators, and mole-drainers, and who was complete master of his art. He always told his two masters who owned and drove the engines:

'I'm master all the week, but you can be master Saturday night.'

When he died the tackle struggled through a season or two, but was soon laid up and ploughed no more. His death was like removing the mainspring from a watch, and how often this happens when a business or farm loses the person who has driven it along and kept the whole show going!

That autumn father heard a rumour that some farms at Sandon, a village some two miles from Chelmsford, were being vacated by their tenant, and he followed that rumour as fast as he could go. The Lodge Farm at East Hanning-field was proving a mixed blessing, and producing a series of bad crops with unfailing regularity, and an opportunity to rent farms on better land was not to be missed.

Uncle Frank was in the middle of a six months' indisposition, owing to having strained his back sack-carrying, and had been ordered complete rest. To top these developments a small farm called Frenches on the Rettendon road fell vacant, and father hired it from a man named Hardy. The weather might be bad and times hard, but father wasn't worrying.

The Sandon farms were owned by the late Mr. Silas

Pledger of Springfield, a great friend of father's, in company with his brother Adolphus. Some time after father began his tactful inquiries he ran into Silas himself one market day in Chelmsford High Street. A highly diplomatic conversation ensued, with both sides hedging hard. Father said Uncle Frank was fed up with the Lodge, and they had 'heard' there were some farms with good land going at Sandon. Silas seemed delighted, and told father he could have the farms at Michaelmas the following year if he liked, and away he went to Hilliards, his agents, to tell them 'the two young Smiths were to have the first offer.'

Uncle Frank was at first rather appalled by father's rashness. If the Sandon deal went through he and father would be farming eleven hundred and fifty acres of land, for the Lodge lease ran till the Michaelmas of 1906. However, after complicated negotiations, which lasted till Lady Day 1905, the Sandon farms were leased to Uncle Frank and father. They consisted of four farms, named Grace's Cross, Sandon Lodge, Dealtrees, and Reasons, and comprised some two hundred odd acres.

The land father and Uncle Frank farmed at this time was therefore made up as follows:

Link House farms . . .	625	acres
The Lodge . . .	250	,,
Frenches . . .	84	,,
Sandon farms . .	200	,,

1,159 acres

This probably doesn't sound much to 'big-time' farmers nowadays, but for two young farmers starting from scratch it wasn't a bad effort.

Michaelmas 1905, after a year of improved weather conditions, saw father and Uncle Frank hard at it, going the round of sales to buy stock and implements for the new farms.

One week father was out every day either to a sale or a market. He covered the more distant sales while Uncle Frank went to those near home, and to the actual sale at Sandon Lodge of the outgoing tenant, Richardson. Each morning father would be round the farms before breakfast, and then away out on his bicycle. They started with bad luck and a bad deal. Father bought a three-year-old colt at a sale at Fyfield, and as soon as they got it home it quietly and quickly died.

Uncle Frank drove over to Link House when he heard the news, and found father in the stable gazing disconsolately at the body of the dead colt.

'What ever are you up to now?' he asked.

Father's feelings were too deep for words, and they turned and went out of the stable together. Farmers don't cry over dead animals. They dig a hole or get hold of the knacker, and that's that!

Next morning father cycled to a sale at Bradwell-on-Sea, a distance of some twenty miles or so. When he arrived he met Mr. Gale, the auctioneer.

'This is strange country for you, John,' he said, giving him a ticket for lunch. 'Go and eat all you can, and then come and do some buying.'

In those days the auctioneers at farm sales provided a good meal for prospective buyers at their own expense. A sale was a sale then. Father went and ate his fill, and came out feeling well disposed towards Mr. Gale. He joined in the bidding for a time to liven things up and help the auctioneer, and then, like the moving finger, moved on, as there seemed to be nothing he wanted.

His next call was at a farm at Southminster, where a sale was to be held next day, but here again, after a thorough inspection of both live and dead stock, he found nothing he wanted or liked. After he had covered three or four miles on his return journey his somewhat fruitless day was completed by a puncture in his back wheel. In the gathering dusk father grappled with it, and he still seems to remember that particular puncture with sour venom.

On the day following this grand tour the actual Sandon Lodge sale was held, but father, leaving this to Uncle Frank, went off to Great Leighs, to a sale at a farm called Moulsham Lodge. Here again his luck was out, the horses, which were what he was mainly interested in, being too much on the small side for his fancy. After a short survey he was off again to a sale at Witham, where he at last found what he wanted. The horses were large and strong, and looked as if they had some work in them. Father bought four, and rode leisurely and contentedly home.

The next day was market day at Chelmsford, and then father rounded off his week by going to a sale at South Hanningfield on the Saturday, where he bought a small bunch of bullocks.

'Good coloury roans they were,' he says reminiscently. He enjoyed that week, and it certainly was a vintage year for sales. 'There were sales galore,' says father, his eye kindling.

Things settled down nicely in the new farms. Uncle Frank moved from the Lodge to Grace's Cross. The weather was good, and all the yards were full of stock.

Then one day towards the end of harvest as father rode over Cut-Elm hill on his way back from Sandon, he saw a cloud of smoke ahead of him, and he passed two old women and then a man hurrying down the road.

'Gooin' to see the fire, sir?' the man called.

'Where is it?' father called back, and then, before the man could reply, he looked again at that cloud of smoke.

'My God!' he said. 'It's my place. Cannon Barns.'

When father got there everything had gone, bar the

house and a small detached piggery. The almost full stack yard and the buildings were razed to the ground, and the men were away up the neighbouring field beating out the flames which were running up the stubble towards some still uncarted traves.

The fire had been started by one of the horseman's sons, who, discovering a box of matches in his father's coat, struck one and set it to the stack on which the men were working. The straw was as dry as tinder, and as the child cried delightedly: 'I 've got a little fire!' the flames sprang up the side of the stack and the men had to jump for their lives. A moment more, with a strong wind fanning the flames, and the whole stack was enveloped. The horseman whose wagon was unloading just got his load away in time with his horse scenting fire and crazy with fright.

After that it was soon over; the rest of the stacks and the buildings were right for the wind, and there was nothing any one could do about it. The flames, with complete and devouring rapidity, swept across from stack to stack, and from stack to old timbered farm as fast as a man could run.

The pond, save for a small pool in the middle, was hard cracked mud, but one of the horsemen kept his head and made the best possible use of that small pool. Running to the stables, which were on the far side of the buildings, he seized armfuls of harness and threw them out of the stable door into the nearby pool. Before the flames began to crackle up the stable thatch he had saved most of the harness of the six horses stabled there.

The yards were luckily empty of stock, and the horses were stabled at Frenches that night. Father says it took the men days to get over the fire, and even admits that it shook him a bit too.

When there was nothing more that could be done, and he had seen the horses safely stabled, father rode slowly home.   As he passed Potter's farm opposite the old 'Plough and Sail,' old Potter was leaning over the gate.

'My God!' he said.   'I was working on top of one of my stacks when the fire came running up the field and, with the wind where it was, I thought we should be for it too. Ah,' he continued, nodding his head, 'fire 's a good servant but a bad master.'

With which cold comfort father went home to bed, but if ever he finds any one smoking about our buildings nowadays, that 's the remark he quotes, considerably embellished, and very forcibly!

As the crops had been good that year the insurance hardly covered their value, and when father and Uncle Frank went to London for the final settlement somewhere about Christmas, the manager of the company gave them a word of advice.

'Look here,' he said, 'always insure over the value rather than under.   Then you 're always on the safe side, and if anything happens you 've no regrets.'

I fancy we 've always been pretty well covered since then.

This same year father's sister Lilian died, leaving three small children.   Father never forgot how mystified the two eldest children were by the sudden arrival of the entire family in full black Victorian funeral panoply.   After the funeral, father accompanied my uncle, Percy Jackson, Lilian's husband, on the famous trip round England, which is often still the subject of rich Saturday night reminiscence.

At Michaelmas the Lodge Farm was finally given up, and a sale held to dispose of surplus 'live and dead stock.' The incoming tenant refused to follow the usual custom of 'taking the corn out.'   When a farm changes hands, the corn belongs to the outgoing farmer, while the straw and chaff are the property of the newcomer, who has to see to the threshing and cart the corn.   Father eventually agreed to do this for three shillings a quarter.   (N.B.—One quarter equals two sacks, each of eighteen stone.)   As coal and

* D

water had to be found for the threshing, this seems a very reasonable sum in these expensive days, when threshing alone costs five shillings a quarter.

The new tenant was a nervous, fussy man, and he exasperated father by continually getting in the way while the wagons were being loaded for fear of a wrong count of the sacks. What father eventually said to him must be reserved for Saturday nights, but it was picturesque, to the point, and commendably brief. It was odd, but afterwards the new tenant just didn't seem to care how many sacks went away in the wagons.

The rebuilding of Cannon Barns was completed by the March of 1909, with some good brick buildings and bullock yards, and a fine Dutch barn. It was a good average year, with plenty of hay and a useful corn crop, and the only trouble occurred during pea-picking, when it rained for some days steadily and consistently. The pickers, some forty or fifty in number, were sleeping in the barns and sheds at Frenches, and as the rain day after day prevented them working for more than an hour or so, their reserves of cash, always small, soon ran out. They were cold, wet, muddy, bedraggled, and hungry. Father realized that the only thing to do was to give them bread in advance of wages, and take a chance on their honesty. He drew the line at beer. He knew them, and he fancied some of them might be inclined to overdraw on their accounts.

He drove round to Sparrow's, the baker's, and asked if he could have some bread.

'You can have a cartload,' said Sparrow, 'but you'll have to be answerable.'

Father accordingly took a cartload, and distributed the loaves to the pickers. They savaged the bread like hungry animals and, as the weather cleared that afternoon, went cheerfully to work to restore their fortunes. They had just got well into their first bags when an exceptionally fierce thunderstorm broke over the field, soaking them all once more.

As a pea-picker rarely has a change of clothing one can imagine what deep feelings he has about 'getting a wet shirt.' The stockman at Frenches found that a surprising number of bags and sacks were missing after the pickers had gone.

The thunderstorm cleared the air, and picking finally went merrily ahead. Father only lost the price of one loaf, for every man but one paid his debt, and that one was probably absent-mindedness after a visit to the 'Plough and Sail.'

On Michaelmas Day 1909 father married my mother, Margaret Rosalie Wace, the second daughter of the Rev. Walter Wace, who was, as mentioned before, the rector of the parish. It was a wretched day of steady rain following a soaking summer. Father never finished carting the hay and, as he walked out of church with his bride on his arm, he saw the men at plough away across the valley, while in the neighbouring fields the corn still stood in sodden traves. The sun shone out in a momentary damp gleam as the happy couple left Chelmsford station, but the glass must still have been set at MUCH RAIN, for when they returned that night from a visit to the theatre they found their hotel room had been flooded by a faulty water pipe. After a week's holiday in Devon, father returned to finish his harvest. As they drove through West Hanningfield on their way back to Link House, the church bells were rung in welcome, which may have cheered father as he saw that the fields were still as full as when he left a week before.

Gradually the corn came in through the short days and the soft October dusk. Stacks stood anywhere handy in the fields, where they were left till the following spring, when the corn was threshed for grinding.

When the first winter frosts came father carted the hay

home for litter.   It was best left till then; the carts didn't
cut such deep ruts in the fields.

In father's memory 1910 is only a prelude to the vintage
year of 1911.   It was coronation year, and a roaring hot
summer.   The winter corn had gone in well, and heavy
land got in well does well, and hot weather suits it.   The
hay crop was heavy and of excellent quality, and was
followed by a bumper crop of peas.   One night a steam
lorry, piled high with the eighty-pound bags then in use,
had its load slip off on its way to Spitalfields market.
Luckily it was near home, and out the wagons had to come
to pick up the bags and get them off in time at Battlesbridge
station.   The pickers were paid one shilling a bag, which is
roughly what they are paid nowadays for a bag half the
size.   Father mostly grew Improved Sickles, Telegraphs,
or Imperial Blues (a fine Napoleonic title, that).   On coronation day some bags disappeared, and though father was
sure of the culprits, he was unable to bring the crime home
to them.   Without doubt the proceeds of the theft disappeared that evening at the 'Ivy House.'

Link House was the scene of great celebrations on coronation day.   Every one in the village attended a church
service at two o'clock.   Every one, that is, with the exception
of one Fred Harmon, who was left behind to grease the
pig and get tea ready in the barn.

Besides tea there were four and a half gallons of beer for
the men, just to keep them happy before the serious business
of the evening began at the 'Ivy House.'   There were
sports in the horse meadow, including an obstacle race over
wagons and under pegged-down pig nets and stack cloths,
and then finally the big event of the afternoon, the ladies'
race for the greasy pig (the course to be decided by the pig).
Half a score of stalwart ladies of the village lined up at the
start amid scenes of tremendous enthusiasm, and the pig,
heavily greased, was released.

Half a dozen wild detours through the cheering and, by now, hysterical crowd, led him to the horse meadow gate, and from there through the farmyard. The field was soon well spread out, but every now and again one of the ladies would put all she knew into a tremendous sprint until, drawing level with the quarry, she threw herself sideways in a loving rugger tackle round his neck. However, time and again this Tetrarch of the farmyard shook himself free and continued on his frantic squealing way, leaving breathless and begreased ladies in his wake. This soon began to thin out the field, few of the followers feeling themselves equal to a second tackle. From the yard the pig careered headlong down the lane, beside the horse-pond, and into the field at the back of the house. Here, feeling probably that though defeated he was not dishonoured, he was caught by a Mrs. Pavitt who, says father, 'always could run like a stag.'

To finish the evening mother gave away the prizes from a wagon, and the four-and-a-half-gallon cask was tilted steeply and drained. One or two of the men, who had been willing helpers with the pouring out and handing round, now seemed to father to be 'three sheets in the wind.' Probably one glass in four as commission on service!

That year's harvest was the finest father ever saw at Link House and, to commemorate it, he and mother paid their visit to Paris. On his return he harvested thirty acres of a clover seed crop, of which he says he never saw a better. A neighbouring farmer, whose crop was a quarter of an acre, told father, who sold it for him: 'My God, it makes my hair stand straight up end.'

Twenty acres of Gate-Post mangold pulled in October proved an immense crop, and great bulky clamps stood all round the field. Gate-Post is a variety which has now completely died out, very coarse, but a heavy cropper. In the same month father bought twenty Lincoln Red cattle from Herbert Page at Colchester. They had a rare lunch and a quart bottle of champagne before the deal. Father says they looked a wonderful bunch of cattle after that lunch.

However, they must have been nearly as good as they looked, for father had them in the yard at Cannon Barns, where they did well, and were soon gone to market. They were followed by another bunch, which again did as well, and were also soon gone. A contributing factor may have been that father and Uncle Frank had bought thirty tons of best English linseed cake at six pounds seven shillings and sixpence per ton, at that year's Essex show, or it may have been that even the cattle felt that they must respond to the fecundity of the year.

When the corn was threshed out at Link House a heap of two hundred quarters of barley stood in the barn waiting to be dressed. This was carted into Chelmsford by the horsemen, who, to make two journeys a day, were paid double wages and given sixpence a journey for expenses, but the old men always said: 'That do give it to your horses terrible!'

While father was enjoying this wonderful summer on the heavy West Hanningfield land, Uncle Frank at Sandon was dried right up on his gravelly soil, and had very light crops indeed, which is the plain explanation of why, whatever happens, there are bound to be some farmers grumbling somewhere and with just cause, one man's weather being another's poison!

The next two years were but pale editions of 1911, and father has little comment to make on them. In 1912 a wet hay-time was followed by an early harvest, though as soon as the corn was cut the weather broke again, and the corn began to grow in the trave. Forty acres of barley which father had down grew particularly badly, and when Uncle Frank came over to Link House one day he looked at the fields in dismay.

'What are you going to do, John?' he said. 'Here you are with your crops down and going to the devil. Why don't you get it threshed, and have it dried somewhere afterwards?'

But father said no. If the crop was threshed now half the corn would stay in the straw. He'd take a chance on the weather breaking.

And break it did the very next day, with a good strong nor'-easter, which dried the crop out well. Father threshed it out in October, and made thirty shillings a quarter of some two hundred quarters.

The year 1913 was indifferent as regards crops, and was notable only for the death of my grandfather, the Rev. Walter Wace, and my arrival. Grandfather died one Sunday morning in January, just as the church bells were ringing for morning service. He had served the parish for fifteen years, and died a greatly beloved man. From what my parents have told me, and also from what I have been told by the old villagers I knew in my childhood, it is one of my greatest regrets that I was never able to know him.

Chelmsford cattle fair was always held on 12th November in those days, and father never missed it. I was born, conveniently enough, at about ten o'clock in the morning, and when my safe arrival had been suitably celebrated, father drove the doctor into Chelmsford, and then prepared to visit the fair. As he drove up the High Street his car, a Belsize, broke down. The garage told him the repairs would take some time and, as he had promised to pay his mother at Sandon a visit on his way home, he told them to make haste, and eventually made his way to the fair.

There were swarms of cattle there, brought by the usual dealers: Connor, the hard-drinking likable Irishman, with whom father and Uncle Frank usually dealt; the Fenners, Walter, William, Golden, and John; Maurice Hughes, the Welshman, who must almost hold the record for the length of time spent in the cattle trade; and many more beside. The drovers were busy and important in their hard high felt hats. Their doyen was a man named Captain, who could almost make the bullocks follow him round the ring to show off their good points.

Sometimes when there was a slack trade the farmers would hold off buying till late in the day, when the dealers were desperate and willing to get rid of their cattle at almost any price rather than have them left on their hands. However, on this occasion trade was good, and father and Uncle Frank had bought cattle from other sources, but, even without a late deal, it was six p.m. before father arrived home again.

Mother took a very poor view of his prolonged absence, and ever since then has been a little inclined to distrust both father's and my own activities at sales.

As soon as I was old enough to understand I was told I ought to know something about dealing. I was born on the right day!

CHAPTER XI

THEY ALL LIVED THERE ONCE

'She's dockety-hi!' old Mrs. Mott would say as she stood in her cottage door watching a village maiden passing up the road with some of the lads. It meant, as far as can be known, flirtatious; and having delivered her weighty judgment she would turn back into the cottage with her old bustle bouncing and the sun glinting on her beaded hair-net. A great character, old Mrs. Mott, with a knowledge of herbs and a stern way with ailments of the stomach. If a child could not take its castor oil Mrs. Mott would be called in, and then a vile brew would be prepared of which the original castor oil was only a minor ingredient, and the whole tasted, if anything, worse than ever. However, it would be drunk and kept down, though whether it was some quality of the brew or Mrs. Mott's personality was never quite decided. The best part of a hundred years ago the schoolmistress at the little village school went by the strikingly apt name of Emma Diaper. One feels that if they ever worked together Mrs. Mott and Miss Diaper must have been a pretty good combination.

Mrs. Mott's services were also greatly sought after as

midwife.   One neighbour of just over forty was to have
her first baby, and, being naturally nervous, was determined
that both Mrs. Mott and the doctor were to be present.
However, the doctor was unavoidably detained, and the
woman gave birth successfully to a fine son before his
arrival.   When he had seen that all was well, and was
downstairs drinking a glass of home-made wine with a
jubilant husband, he turned to Mrs. Mott and said:

'Well, Mrs. Mott, I really must congratulate you.   Where
did you get all your knowledge from?'

Mrs. Mott looked at him stonily.

'Where 'd you get yourn?' she said.

Fifty yards up the road from Mrs. Mott's, past the 'Ivy
House' and the wheelwright's yards, stands the blacksmith's shop.   Passers-by, however, may delay a minute
on their way to the smithy as, seeing the tumbril cart that
is to be repaired standing neglected in the wheelwright's
yard, they glance through the high windows of his shop.
The bright wood of the freshly planed coffin planks catches
their eye.

'I 'll be able to get on with them wheels agin to-morrow,'
they hear the wheelwright say.

Soon after grandfather died father drove a pony cart
with very worn tyres up to the smithy to have the tyres
'cut.'   Old Mr. Parnell, the blacksmith, was over at the
'Ivy House' relaxing after a heavy morning's shoeing, and
father was asked to wait.   Soon Mr. Parnell emerged, and
made his way slowly up the road.   He said 'Good morning'
to father, and looked at the cart.   He smacked his lips,
though whether reminiscently of the bar or in consideration
of the cart wheels was uncertain.

Eventually he spoke again.   'Wit bought, me boy, is
better than wit taught, but don't buy it too dear,' and he
passed on into the smithy.

Father, gazing at the wheels, saw suddenly what he

meant. The tyres were too worn to pay for repairing, what was needed was a set of new tyres. Since then, whenever he has made a mistake or had a bad deal, he always says:

'Never mind, I bought wit, even if it was a little dear.'

Almost all the old farm workers had a ready natural wit, which seems less noticeable with mechanical workers to-day, tractor drivers and such, than with those engaged with horses and stock. Every horseman, now as then, is supposed to plough an acre a day. One morning as father rode round the farms he saw a horseman from Cannon Barns named John Doe sitting on his plough in one of the fields.

'Don't make your acres too big, John,' father said by way of reminder.

'No, sir,' said John quickly. 'I won't do that, the b——s are plenty big enough a'ready.'

It's a story recounted among horsemen with great relish.

No one knows why, but nobody really likes 'drag-raking.' Drag-raking is pulling along the deep-toothed, five-foot-wide wooden drag-rake behind the wagon, picking up the horse-rakings at the end of hay time or harvest. It is not hard work, but perhaps it is disliked for its monotony, and it does entail a good deal of walking.

The dislike in which it is held is shown in another story of the same John Doe. He was the last of the gang to arrive; one man was in the wagon ready to start loading, two more stood ready with their pitchforks. Father, standing by, gave the drag-rake to John.

'You can drag-rake, can't you, John?' he said pleasantly, with a wink at the others.

John surveyed the large expanse of grassland with the long rows of rakings.

'I've got plenty of b—— chance,' he said gloomily.

If a local inhabitant or any one belonging to a neigh-bouring village had some peculiarity or accomplishment that made him a character it would be talked of, repeated, and appreciated by all and sundry. Life now has broadened and hastened. Time is shorter and there is more to see and hear: the cinema, the wireless, the papers. It is to be hoped that, for these things, the full appreciation of simple things by simple men will not be lost.

There was James Oddy, the shoemaker, who would guarantee a pair of boots to keep the water out for a year for fifteen shillings. There was Root, the great fiddler, who at festive seasons would enter the public houses and play a tune then, stopping, put the loud question:

'All they that play to-night shall drink both free and good?'

If the landlord's answer was favourable the night would be merry, and the men with their heavy boots would be dancing the old dances as lightly as many highly paid artists, until perhaps balance was gone and then only song remained. For beer was tuppence a pint, and it was Crabb's beer too—beer of which they said a stranger could only drink two pints before he must fight or go home to his wife.

There was Sam Cooper, whom they called 'Ideas,' who would turn his hand to anything, but whose specialities were mole-catching and thatching. He was remembered for a pig-killing when one pig would not die. Though all life seemed extinct, the high-pitched shrieking note continued. Sam took quick measures, and then said sternly to the pig:

'You 'll die presently, won't you?'

The sequel to this incident was a meeting one evening of Sam's friends and cronies at the 'Ivy House.' Sam was not present and was, therefore, greatly surprised a week or so later on St. Valentine's day, for there on his doorstep was a carved model of himself and a pig which he was attempting to 'stick,' together with the inscription: 'My valentine, you 'll die presently, won't you?'

Bill Newman, who worked with the local threshing gang, was an expert rat-catcher. At each farm the gang visited he would agree with the farmer how much was to be paid per tail, a halfpenny or a penny perhaps; then he was responsible for collecting all the rats killed by the gang and sharing the money out afterwards. At one farm, at which the owner was known to be 'a bad pay,' Bill was 'had' one year. When he took the tails round to the back door at night-time the owner was out and Bill never got his money. However, Bill bided his time and, when the same farm was visited the following year, he made no bargain. Instead he caught the rats alive. The stack was infested. Time after time Bill would dive his hand into one of the short holes with which the stack was riddled to grasp an obscure naked tail. Out would come the rat, with Bill twirling it like a propeller to stop it from biting him, and then quickly he dropped it into a sack. That night the farmer, thinking perhaps that as no bargain had been made he was safe, went out into the yard just as the stack was finished.

Bill Newman, dragging his heaving, squeaking sack, approached him.

'Evenin', master,' he said, 'how 'bout they rat tails this year?'

'We didn't agree anything 'bout them this year, Bill,' said the farmer.

'You don't reckon you 're a-goin' to pay for them, then?' Bill asked quietly.

'No, Bill,' was the reply.

Bill made no answer. Pulling out his shut knife he cut the string round the mouth of the sack. Before the farmer could stop him he shot out the rats, between twenty-five and thirty of them, and away they ran, through the feet of the rest of the gang who stood around, slinking grey shadows, into the darker shadows of the buildings. As they went the roaring lusty laughter of the threshing gang followed them. The further remarks between the farmer and Bill are not recorded.

Mrs. Tyler, who lived at Cannon Barns, found the times hard. Ten shillings a week with nine children to feed often meant short commons, but there were many families in the same straits, and many expedients for making both ends meet.

'O' course,' the old people say, speaking of the children, 'o' course, a lot on 'em died.'

On baking days the oven, standing in the garden, would be filled with dry bushes which would be set alight and replenished till the oven was hot enough. Then the ashes would be raked out, and the bread would go in. Beautiful bread it was, which kept wonderfully fresh, and was never eaten till it was a week old.

When tea was short on winter nights Mrs. Tyler would toast a piece of bread in front of the kitchen fire till both sides were black. Then she would pour boiling water on it. At least it was almost the right colour, and anyway it was hot. Sometimes, too, they had 'brown sugar pudding,' dough with brown sugar on it.

It was nice, the children said, when they got older and began to earn a bit. It was the first time in their lives that they wore new clothes, and not somebody else's passed on to them.

Pea-picking was one thing the women looked forward to. It meant a bit of a change and some company for a few days, and, more important, it meant a bit of extra money; enough to pay for the children's boots for the winter, and perhaps a bit besides. Several acres of peas were always grown on the Link House farms, and Mr. Ratcliff, who farmed Frenches, near Cannon Barns, for many years, also grew a considerable amount. A field of peas and the chance of extra money after a hard winter must have meant as much to these women as water to a thirsty desert traveller.

Sometimes some of the men would take a day off and come picking. While the work went quickly on, good-humoured shouts and laughter would echo backwards and forwards along the line of pickers. One local bachelor, who had been courting for nearly twenty years, always came picking. He had, he said, got to earn a bit extra to get wed with. Every time he finished a bag he bumped it hard on the ground.

'There,' he would say, 'there's another knob for the bedstead.'

People remembered Mr. Keeble, the hay buyer, by the sealskin cap he always wore. He operated from Battles-bridge, where the barges which he hired came up the Crouch to load the hay he bought on his rounds. Twice a day to Battlesbridge was a wagoner's work from West Hanningfield, loading the hay from one of the farm stackyards and un-loading it into the capacious hold of *Bertie* or *Violet*.

Each of the horsemen had his own wagon, and took great pride in its appearance and running. Some wagons just naturally seem to run better than others, but all require plenty of greasing and attention for road work. Sam Tyler had a piece of decorative ironwork on the front of his wagon.

'You know my wagon,' said Sam, 'that's got a bit of fluradiddley on the front!'

A great majority of the girls went into service when they left school, and would bring home to the cottages tales of high goings-on in the servants' hall, and of the strange eccentricities and habits of the gentry. In a few years, however, most of them would be married and settled down in their own cottages, leaving only a few to become faithful old retainers, their lives dedicated to the comfort of others.

One local gentleman possessed a cook of whom he was justly proud. She was, as he told his friends, a treasure.

It was only after many years of service, when she not only ran the household, but ruled it, that she developed the strange habit of going downstairs far earlier in the morning than her duties necessitated. Sometimes, it seemed to her employer, she went downstairs almost in the middle of the night. Nothing was said, but, waking one morning in the cold dawn hours, he heard the cook's footsteps passing quickly down the corridor.

For half an hour he lay and considered. Then, his curiosity getting the better of him, he got up and crept downstairs. Near the bottom of the staircase he stopped. The dining-room door was open, there was a good fire going, a comfortable meal on the table, and a bottle of his best vintage port. Fascinated, he watched. The cook's meal was finished now, and as she stood up in front of the fire at peace with the world, she spoke aloud:

'I've ate well, now I'll work well!'

The gentleman turned and crept back upstairs. After all, he thought, she's quite right.

Sometimes, too, the women working in the fields had a strange tale to tell. There was a heavy late frost one May which had 'laid' a strong field of winter beans near Cannon Barns as flat as a meadow. Mrs. Doe, who was hoeing the field, went to work as usual. Cold it was, she thought, and a pity to see a fine crop like they beans spoiled.

She got quickly to work to warm herself up and, as she worked, was soon thinking of other things. The sun rose slowly. Mrs. Doe took off her coat and got to work again. Suddenly a sharp crack like a whip-lash startled her. Then another, and another, until the whole field sounded like several erratic machine guns. The warmth of the sun was reaching the bean stalks and, as it reached them, they cracked and straightened. Mrs. Doe dropped her hoe and hurriedly left the field. Reaching home safely she told her neighbour of her strange experience.

'That warn't no place for me,' she said. 'That very near scairt the life out o' me!'

Though the bean field revived and produced a fair crop every stalk was kinked as a reminder of that late frost in May.

''Course, my father was independent,' said the old cottage woman as she stood in her doorway looking towards Partridge's and the Sandon Brook. 'Always said he liked change. He worked for three or four farmers in the village when I was a girl, but o' course we never moved outside the parish. You see that field across the valley by Partridge's? Road Field they call that, used to be a road run across there, and an old woman, she was near ninety when I was a girl, told me there used to be some long, low, brick buildings there what people called 'The Smugglers,' though none on us never knew why. There's four fields called "Gomer's" there, too: Gomer's Four Acres, Gomer's Five Acres, Gomer's Eight Acres, and Gomer's Ten Acres, though who Gomer was we never knew neither.

'I rec'lect when we was living down at Partridge's, father always used to take us for a walk on Sunday evenings. We looked forward to that. We'd walk as far as the bridge over the brook, and then father he'd say: "Well, which is it this week, shall we goo up the brook or shall we goo down?"

'And o' course,' she said, 'sometimes we'd goo up and sometimes we'd goo down. That was lovely down there in the summer.'

CHAPTER XII

THE WAR YEARS

THE little breakfast-room at Link House was bathed in sunlight one warm July morning in 1914, and my great-uncle, Alfred Wace, and his wife Amy, were reading the morning papers over their breakfasts with a preoccupied air. Three or four fields away a binder could be heard making its first cautious round of a field of winter oats, and from the hen house across the yard a triumphant hen announced the completion of another good day's work.

Aunt Amy looked up from her paper.

'If we 're not careful,' she said, 'this means a European war.'

And so the ripples of the far-off incident at Sarajevo disturbed faintly the placid Essex farmyard.

The corn stood high that year. In Broadover it was up to Richard Wace's shoulders, and he stood six foot two in his socks.

'A wonderful crop, John,' he said to father, as they walked round the farms. 'I only wish things looked as well everywhere else.'

Day after day Charlie Doe, a horseman at Cannon Barns,

who was an Army reservist, asked father anxiously if calling-up notices had appeared in the papers. Then, suddenly, he was gone, and the storm had broken. The next father heard of Charlie was that he had been taken prisoner at Mons. Four and a half years later he returned to Cannon Barns with many a tale to tell, and to pick up the reins he had dropped so long before. Three others of father's men left the same morning as Charlie, and two never came back.

It is at this point that, to my great dismay, I found father's memory beginning to fail. A memory that could recall every incident of crop and weather from 1877 to 1914 suddenly found events crowding in too fast for accurate recording. The even tenor of the country round was broken, and seed-time and harvest, that had been slow-moving happenings, now good, now bad, became mere incidents in the rush of hurried days. Father's memory never recovered, and however much one questions him concerning the years 1914 to 1940 he always reverts to the golden age of thirty to sixty years ago, 'when,' as he says, 'farming was farming, and not the subsidized, bolstered-up, neglected government puppet it has become since the war.'

However, certain incidents remain in father's brain and, even if they be no longer exactly chronological, they may help to complete his memory picture of his long life.

The outbreak of war thoroughly unsettled many of the threshing gangs and farm workers, whose heads were immediately filled with thoughts of increased wages; and a threshing gang which was working at Hophedges Farm became thoroughly disorganized. Father had to keep it going with several of his own men, and himself spent one day behind the machine sacking up the corn, the sacker spending the day partly in the 'Ivy House' and partly in a state of beatific unconsciousness under a hedge.

One hot September Friday in 1914 the farmers on their way home from market pulled up their gigs and pony carts,

in father's case a Belsize two-seater motor car, in which he
had invested the year before, to read a notice stuck up in
the window of the *Essex Weekly News*. They read it, and
then slowly turned away, and, whipping up their horses,
drove on home. The notice contained the first news of the
retreat from Mons, and mother says she never forgot her
feelings as she drove home through the golden autumn
country. It was as though a blow had been struck at the
very foundations of the old Victorian and Edwardian
world, and to this day a certain section of road in Galleywood reminds mother of her feelings that afternoon.

Father soon became a special constable, and later on inspected farms where extra ploughing had to be done for the
War Agricultural Committee. He did this in company
with a neighbouring farmer named Tom Blyth, with whom
he often also combined in special constable duties.

In 1916 a farm called Tinsley, of some two hundred
acres, close to Link House, was taken over by the Government, and father was asked to farm it. At the same time
father's foreman and right-hand man, Bill Snell, was called
up, and father had to go before the tribunal in Chelmsford
to plead his case.

'If you take him,' he said, 'they can have Tinsley back.
I can't do impossibilities.'

Snell was allowed to remain, and is with us to this day—
one of the best and most versatile farm workers that ever
lived. Father appeared before the tribunal on many other
occasions in an attempt to keep men on the land.

'If you want the food we must have the men to produce
it,' he always vehemently declared. 'You've got to make
up your mind whether fighting or food is the most important, and nobody's going to put up much of a fight
with an empty belly.'

Father made a clean start with Tinsley, which had been
badly neglected, by steam-ploughing the whole farm. But

after a good hay-time the weather took a hand with heavy rain, and the water stood in the furrows when the corn was carted.

In 1917 the labour situation was somewhat eased when four German prisoners were sent to work on Tinsley. One, whom father called Jock, was a good hard-working fellow, but the other three were only fair. Father found the right recipe for a good day's work was to give them some beer, which he often did with excellent results. He also overlooked the fact that considerable quantities of small 'chat' potatoes went back to camp with them in the evenings. Their midday meal consisted only of potatoes, which mother cooked for them, and which they ate with their fingers, until, one day, Jock plucked up courage to come to the back and ask: 'Might they have the honour of a spoon?'

Father's duties as special constable had occasional high spots, as West Hanningfield lay pretty well on the Zeppelins' route to London, and it was strongly rumoured that lights were flashed from some of the many woods in the district to guide them on their way. For this reason father was often warned to spend a night 'wood-watching,' and though he himself never saw a light, and nobody was ever caught, his conviction that lights were flashed remained unshakable. One evening he remembers with some warmth. He was warned at market, it being a Friday, to watch Well Wood that night. He began a solitary vigil at about seven o'clock, and was just beginning to get thoroughly chilled and disgruntled when at about nine a shadowy figure approached him. Father was just about to pounce when the figure, in the friendly voice of Tom Blyth, said:

'That you, John?'

Father said yes, it was him, and dam' cold he was too. Tom Blyth, a man of few words, simply said 'Right,' and disappeared again into the darkness.   However, he returned within half an hour bringing in his pocket a bottle of orange gin.   Father and Tom Blyth stayed in Well Wood for some time, and then, in a spirit of indissoluble comradeship, went for a walk up to the South Hanningfield 'Windmill,' not because it was open, but just because they felt like a good walk anyway.   From here they decided to call it a day, and departed to their respective homes.   Father's only other recollection of the night is having a little trouble with his bicycle as he was passing the church!

On another occasion he was on patrol, after a busy week on the farm, for the fourth or fifth night running.   At the top of the village, near the 'Compasses,' he saw something grey in the hedge, which turned out to be Mr. Jell, one of the villagers.   It was a fine clear night, and Mr. Jell was waiting for the inevitable Zeppelin.

'They 'll come to-night, Mr. Smith,' he said, 'as sure as my name 's Jell.   What about a quick one?'

Now my father never has a drink unless he is really thirsty or really needs it, and he certainly needed it that night.   He had a quick one at the 'Compasses,' and then cycled slowly back to Link House.

'They 're sure to come to-night,' he said to mother, 'and if I sit down I shall go to sleep.'

Mother advised a hot bath, which he duly took, and then went and sat upright on his bed and started talking to mother.   The next thing he remembers is a violent hammering at the front door, and a handful of pebbles against the bedroom window.   He looked quickly at his watch; it was three in the morning, and he had missed one of the most amazing sights of the war.

A Zeppelin had been brought down in flames near Norsey Wood at Billericay, some five miles away, and almost the entire neighbourhood had turned out to see the huge pre-historic leviathan stagger its last few miles through the sky.

The next morning the whole countryside for miles was covered with a fine grey dust from the burnt envelope, and many of the farm boys were missing from work. They arrived back in the village about midday, riding slowly, their bikes covered with souvenirs.

West Hanningfield was one of the first villages to start a women's institute in the Chelmsford area, and Mrs. Arthur Watt, the Canadian founder of the movement, came down and stayed a night at Link House for the branch's inaugural meeting. Nearly every Sunday too, as the war drew on, father fetched wounded soldiers from Chelmsford hospital, and brought them out to Link House to tea. I have dim recollections of toddling round after the men in blue as father showed them round the bullock yards after tea.

In 1917 father had his second experience of a farm fire. A hot haystack at Tinsley suddenly burst into roaring flame, and everything except the house and stables was burnt to the ground. The fire, not unnaturally, was attributed by many of the villagers to sabotage by the German prisoners, but father absolved them from all blame. A hot haystack catches up with all farmers from time to time, for if they want to obtain hay of any quality the stack needs to get a little warm. Father had been watching this stack anxiously for days, and awaiting his chance for the heat to abate a little and then turn it over. The danger of turning over a hot stack is that when the air gets to the greatest point of heat she goes up instantaneously from combustion. However, in this case the stack made the first move, and that was that.

In 1917 the Germans began to make daylight raids in London with Gotha aircraft, and father as special constable was supposed to forward the news of their approach. He remembers riding along the top of twelve acres at Cannon Barns one morning and hearing the distant drone of their engines. Turning his horse he galloped headlong across the fields to the telephone at West Hanningfield post office. These Paul Revere rides which father made seem to have foreshadowed our present-day Observer Corps, and a comparison certainly shows how the speed of aircraft has increased. The planes of to-day would have been over and almost out of sight before father had turned his horse.

As the year drew on the demand for a greater acreage of arable land became more insistent, and mother was surprised one afternoon when one of the local 'county' gentry called to see her. This good lady had previously hardly acknowledged our existence, and her sudden geniality and warm invitation to tea were rather surprising. However, light gradually dawned when we realized that she expected father to order the ploughing up of the parkland in front of her house.

Father is always sceptical about the value of ploughing land unless it is of proved worth. 'What's the use,' he says, 'of saying you've got so many acres under the plough unless you know you are really going to get a worth-while crop?' Some land which was ploughed up under the War Agricultural Committee's orders in the Rettendon district failed to produce more than three sacks of corn to the acre. 'Plough up the good land and do it well!' is father's maxim for this war as for the last.

The heavy harvest of 1917 saw father mobilizing all available labour in the parish to get it under cover. In one field of barley the straw was so long and 'laid' that the binder was useless, and father was obliged to use two grass-mowers, and even then these would only cut it one way. Father's 'Johnny Wobblers' gang (the Essex name for a gang of makeshift irregular harvesters; its correct interpretation cannot, unfortunately, be given here) were hard at it, raking back the swaths of barley to make lanes for the mowers' empty return journey. Eventually the field was cut, and father resolved to thresh it out as soon as it was 'made' enough. The morning that the threshing machine arrived was hot and sultry, with thunder grumbling in the distance; however, there was nothing for it but to chance the storm's holding off and begin threshing. Just as the machine started up and the first wagon load drew up alongside the barn work, the storm broke. Father got under the wagon, and lay down to watch the rain pelting steadily on the quickly sodden barley. A depressing sight, and one well known to all farmers. The rain was so heavy that it came clean through the load and dripped down father's neck through cracks in the wagon's floor-boards. At such moments in a farmer's life his feelings are far too deep for words!

The storm, fortunately, did not herald a break in the weather, and father, remobilizing the 'Johnny Wobblers,' was able to cart and thresh the field several days later.

At Michaelmas 1918 a farmer named Stacey took Tinsley Farm over from the Government, and this relieved father of a part of his extra labour. As he walked through the farmyard with Hugh Hilliard, the auctioneer, just before the commencement of the Tinsley Farm sale, Hugh turned to him and said:

'You'll see, John, this war won't last much longer!'

Some six weeks later, on the morning of 11th November, the news reached us at Link House. As father came riding in from the fields to lunch I went running down the yard to meet him with excited yells:

'Daddy, daddy, the war's over!'

The sound of distant jubilant church bells and the shrill whistles of threshing-machine engines came in from all directions across the quiet fields. That night the 'Ivy House' was cleared out, and next morning one of the men, who seemed not quite himself, remarked feelingly to father: 'That's a good job we don't get peace every day!'

E

CHAPTER XIII

STRANGE TALES THEY TELL OF TOWN

It would seem only fair to point out that an agricultural district, for all its placid ways and unhurried days, may have as dramatic a background as any gold-rush town or roaring tempestuous city.

Take, for instance, the Greyhound Inn at Chelmsford, which stood at the top of the High Street, on the present site of a branch of Barclays Bank. It was a coaching inn, and a pleasant place in 1752 with a genial elderly landlord, who was a bachelor. His patrons were all agreed that it was a pity when, in that same year, he fell violently in love with and married a beautiful girl many years younger than himself. Not that she wasn't a pleasant enough lass, the customers agreed, adding over the rims of their pint pots that she must have married him for the money and position. The customers were all agreed again when, a month or so later, the landlord committed his second error by engaging an exceptionally handsome young ostler.

Mine hostess seemed well disposed towards the young man, and was, in fact, carrying on a passionate liaison with him before many weeks had passed. The affair, however, was conducted with great skill. The customers and staff had hardly the barest grounds for rumour. They noticed that the landlord seemed at times to be worried and ill at ease.

'That's what marriage does fer yer!' they said, laughing, and ordered another pint.

It was something of a shock, therefore, to all concerned when, early one morning a few weeks later the young wife rushed downstairs in violent hysterics.

Her poor darling husband had died in bed, she cried, between sobs and wild laughter, there before her very eyes. And him to bed the night before as well as ever and very loving. Oh, what had she done to deserve this?

However, at last she allowed herself to be quieted and her wild paroxysms gave way to calm grief. The atmosphere of death hung heavy over the 'Greyhound.' The customers were quiet, shocked, and greatly surprised.

'But there,' as they said after a while, 'it just shows yer, here to-day and gone to-morrow!'

After the funeral the depressing atmosphere was allowed to lift slowly. Mine hostess was to carry on the inn and, as she said to one of her regular customers:

'Business is business, and we must do our best to carry on and look cheerful!'

Things, in fact, soon became very cheerful, and it was not many months before the lady of the house had married the handsome ostler, and settled down to run the 'Greyhound' with him.

The marriage caused a considerable stir in the town, following, as it did, so soon after the landlord's tragic death. Might have waited a bit longer, people said; hardly cold in his grave, he is; but there, young blood runs hot, I suppose!

The scandal died quickly, for the new landlord and his wife made the 'Greyhound' a pleasant, busy place. There were horses for hire, the stage coaches rumbled in and out, and the rooms were full of talk and laughter and the clink of pewter. Business was good.

It was seventeen years later when a stranger came to the town. He stabled his horse and, having time on his hands, decided to take a look at the sights of Chelmsford. Eventually he reached the church of St. Mary (now Chelmsford Cathedral). He walked slowly and meditatively round the inside and then, coming out into the graveyard, started to walk round the exterior. Half way round he found the sexton, busy with a half-dug grave. Struck by the extremely large number of bones the sexton was turning up he stopped to watch.

In those days no one could count on lying in his grave for more than twenty years, which was the limit laid down before the ground could be used again. The bones thrown up would be placed in the charnel house and, of course, there was always a market for them with the medical gentlemen, and an exceptionally good trade for teeth. Space was short in St. Mary's churchyard and, thought the sexton, the difference between seventeen and twenty was only three years, and what was three years for a dead man to worry about? So it happened that the grave he was digging was in the ground where the late landlord of the 'Greyhound' had been buried seventeen years before.

The stranger moved nearer and spoke.

'A large number of bones you find,' he said.

'Yes, sir,' replied the sexton. 'We throws 'em up, we throws 'em up!'

As he spoke his next spadeful landed at the foot of the stranger, and from the earth rolled a skull. The stranger bent and picked it up, and the sexton, leaning on his spade, spoke reminiscently.

'Nice chap he was, sir; knew him well. Used to be the landlord o' the "Greyhound," across the road. Died sudden, he did. Many a pint I've had . . .'

The stranger suddenly interrupted him.

'What the devil's this?' he asked, and from the back of the landlord's skull he drew a long rusty nail.

The sexton could hardly scramble from the grave quick enough. After examining the grisly find he stopped only to ask the stranger his name and address, and then went direct to the house of a nearby magistrate.

It was an hour or so later when the sexton made his appearance at the 'Greyhound' with a message for the landlord. The magistrate, he said (who was called perhaps Mr. Gepp), would be obliged if the landlord would call round at his house as soon as was convenient.

The landlord was pleased. Hurrying out into the yard, where so many years before he had started his career as an ostler, he ordered one of the best horses to be harnessed to a chaise. Business, already good, was getting better. Hiring out horse and chaise to the gentry was a profitable business.

On arrival at Mr. Gepp's house he was somewhat surprised to be asked in, but thought only that it augured better than ever. Mr. Gepp was waiting for him in his library. He greeted him civilly.

'Well, sir,' asked the landlord, 'what can I do for you?'

Mr. Gepp opened a drawer in his desk and, taking out the skull, slowly withdrew the nail.

'What do you know about this?' he asked quietly.

The shock was too great, and the landlord collapsed on the floor in a dead faint. When he recovered he made a complete confession, and was then removed in custody. The same process was then repeated with his wife, who also confessed to the deed. In due course the couple were convicted of murder, and were hanged on the gibbet by Longstomps Stile on the Galleywood road.

It was some forty or fifty years ago when a gentleman living near Longstomps was presented with a new pair of garden gates by a friend. As they dug the post-holes they came upon human remains which were identified as probably those of felons lying in their unhallowed grave, near the gibbet on which they were hanged.

And so, perhaps, the bones of the landlord and his wife were disturbed by chance, as had been those of the man they murdered so many years before.

Moulsham Hall, which stood not far from Longstomps Stile, and to the left of the London road, was also the scene of strange happenings in the year 1830. It was a magnificent mansion in the Palladian style, and had for long been a principal seat of the Mildmays, a great Chelmsford family.

In that year the then baronet, Sir Henry Mildmay, was greatly troubled by the public's use of a right of way which ran through the centre of his spacious lawns and parkland. He gave orders that entrances to this path be closed at his parkland boundaries. The fences erected by his men were torn down. He ordered their re-erection repeatedly, only to see them repeatedly destroyed and the path in still more general use. The public's back was properly up, and the feud was on.

At length Sir Henry, naming those whom he thought to be the principal instigators or offenders, brought the matter to court. Here, however, he found even the law of the land unfavourable to him and, though he carried the case up to the High Court, it finally went against him.

Sir Henry's anger at his defeat was so great that he never returned to Moulsham Hall. Instead he ordered the complete demolition of the mansion. Every stick and stone was pulled down and removed, and the park, which had caused the trouble, changed back to farm land. All that remained was one small length of red-brick garden wall, standing alone, a reminder of past glories.

Reverting from mansion to inn again, it was the 'Bell' in Chelmsford which was the scene of more dramatic happenings in the seventeen-fifties. The 'Bell' stands next to the corn exchange in Tindal Square, and though not now in use, was ever a popular place for farmers to meet and put up their horses and carts.

The names of the landlord and two farmers concerned in this story are long forgotten, but perhaps we may call the farmers Shaw and Brown.

Shaw, the first to arrive, was in early that Friday. He had a good lot of sheep to sell, he told the landlord, who was standing in the yard, as the ostler took his horse and cart. Trade was good that morning, and he was soon back at the 'Bell,' and asking for the landlord. The landlord was in his cosy back parlour, with its door half-masked by green curtain and crown glass window, the long church-warden pipes on the wall, and a bottle of something 'special' for favoured customers.

Shaw was ushered in, had a glass of the 'special,' and made his request.

'I've got a tidy bit more business to do to-day, landlord,' he said, 'one way and another, and I was wonderin' if you'd be so kind as to look after this for me while I'm about the town?'

And with that he produced a skin bag containing one hundred and fifty pounds, the proceeds of his morning's sale. The landlord expressed his willingness, and Shaw, easy in his mind, went back to business.

It was not long after Shaw had left that Brown arrived. Brown was something of a lad, always well dressed, and fond of a good horse. This morning he was riding what he himself described as 'a really classy nag.' It was well known in the local hunting field, and had done well when matched against other farmers' and gentlemen's horses. Brown saw to it that his horse was carefully stabled and then left, saying that he might be late.

Not long afterwards Shaw returned, his business completed, and after claiming his money, left for home.

As his cart rumbled out of the 'Bell' entrance the landlord

lost no time. He was in difficulties from which there seemed no way out, creditors were pressing and things looked ugly. That hundred and fifty pounds under the seat cushion in Shaw's cart would just put things right. Going to his little back parlour he fetched his pistol, and then went straight to the stable where Brown's 'classy nag' was standing. It was well known that horse dealers were in the habit of leaving their horses at the 'Bell,' and that the landlord, for a consideration, would try out a horse for a gentleman. Nobody would be any the wiser for his riding up the town. And so, saddling up, he was quickly gone.

He overtook Shaw some two miles out of Chelmsford, on the Roxwell road, shot him in the back, took the money from under the seat, and turned his horse for home. He was back again in the 'Bell' only some twenty minutes after he had left. Stabling Brown's horse he gave it a quick rub down. Lathered and steaming it stood there, its sides heaving. The landlord eyed it with misgiving. If its owner were to find his horse in such a state the game would be up, but Brown was a gay lad, and in the habit of leaving town late on market day. He left the stable quickly, meaning to hide the money in his back parlour, and then resume his grooming of the horse.

Then, suddenly, chance was against him. As he left the parlour he heard Brown's voice. Something had happened in the course of his business to upset him, and he was announcing his intention of returning home at once. The landlord hurried into the bar. Drawing Brown aside, he whispered:

'There's a bottle of something extra in my room to-night. I'd like you to try it!'

'No, thank you, landlord. It's home for me to-night, and the sooner the better,' said Brown, and nothing that the landlord could say would stop him. He followed him down the yard, still talking frantically.

Brown threw open the stable door, stood, stared, and then started to swear. Who the hell had been riding his horse? What sort of an inn was this? This 'ud cost the landlord something. By God, he 'd a mind to . . .

The landlord protested fiercely. He had no knowledge of it. He 'd find out. For a moment he hoped it meant no more than a violent row and the loss of a customer, but fate was still against him. The ostler, hearing the altercation, came walking up the yard, waited for a pause in the shouting, realized that the blame might be his, and made his way forward.

'Why, master,' he said, 'I was down the bottom o' the yard not fifteen minutes agoo, and I saw you yerself come ridin' in on that hoss lathered up a sweat, and I wondered whatever was the matter.'

At that Brown's fury broke its limit. He railed and cursed, and the landlord began to cower under his anger. The shouting now attracted the attention of an officer of the law in Tindal Square, who bustled down the 'Bell' yard.

Seeing him, Brown and the landlord began to tell their stories together, but the officer was after bigger game.

'Never mind, never mind,' he said. 'Have you heard the news, landlord? They 've found your customer, Mr. Shaw, murdered on the Roxwell road. Laid in the middle of the road he did . . .'

Suddenly he saw the sweating horse.

'How 'd that horse get like that?' he asked.

Suddenly the landlord found the eyes of the law, of Brown, and of the ostler upon him. It was too much. The confession broke from him there and then. The hundred and fifty pounds were found in the back parlour, and the landlord too was duly hanged on the gibbet at Longstomps Stile. His only memorial was an oak which stood on the roadside near the scene of his crime. 'Hangman's Oak,' people called it.

* E

CHAPTER XIV

THE WEATHER

'A SATURDAY's moon and a Sunday's full' is what father looks for every Christmas when the firms with which he deals send him either calendars or farming diaries. As soon as the first diary arrives a day or two before Christmas father sits down to it, and hunts for this portent, which, being translated, means a new moon falling on a Saturday and coming to the full on a Sunday. If he finds it, he shakes his head, and the month it falls in is marked off as being bound to bring foul weather, for the full couplet runs as follows:

> A Saturday's moon and a Sunday's full
> Never did no good and never 'ull.

This is no idle threat, and if father at Christmas finds these circumstances arriving, say, next July, he looks grave and says:

'You 'll see. July 'll be wet.'

And wet July is. This probably sounds pretty far-fetched. I laughed at it for years, but it works out again and again, and it can't always be coincidence.

I 've been farming myself for twelve years now, and

rather fancy myself as following in the family tradition of weather prophecy. What usually happens, however, is that when I think all the signs and portents point to a wet day to-morrow, I say to father:

'Looks like rain coming.'

Father just glances at the sky and says: 'No, boy, it won't rain,' and, of course it doesn't rain, and vice versa.

Many of father's sayings about the weather are those found in weather calendars in old-fashioned stationers', but it is when he quotes them that they come to life. A bright January with the meadows an emerald green brings forth the remark:

> If the grass grows green in Janiveer
> It grows the worse for it all the year.

If the corn looks well at the same time he complains that it is 'winter-proud.'

'I never like to see the corn look too well this time of the year,' he says. As Lent draws to a close he quotes:

> Rain on Good Friday and wet Easter Day
> Plenty of grass but little good hay,

And if the weather is doubtful he spends an anxious Easter.

When, one April morning, the shepherd bends his head against an icy wind from the east as he carries a pair of new-born lambs to the shelter of the straw-hurdle fold, and old Harry Cox, our seventy-six-year-old cowman, blows on his once frost-bitten hands in the cow shed, then father comes puffing and blowing in to breakfast.

'My hands are so cold I could cry, only I'm ashamed,' he says. 'This is the black-bush winter. The first thing Harry Cox said to me this morning was: "The owd black-bush is hatchin'."'

Then for three or four days while the blackthorn buds are bursting, we may be sure of cold weather until the white splashes of blossom burst along the still dark hedgerows.   The 'black-bush winter' would seem to be the winter equivalent of 'St. Martin's little summer' in the autumn.

On a sunny April day, when the wind is strong from the west, and one can feel everything round growing, father says, rather joyously:

> When April blows his horn
> 'Tis good for hay and corn.

When I complain about the cold springs we usually so thoroughly enjoy in East Anglia, father always quotes an old farmer he knew in his youth: 'Cold May, mate, cold May, that's what we want.   You'll see the wheat run well then when you're threshing.'

An old neighbour of ours had a saying:

> When the cuckoo sings on an empty bough
> Keep your hay and sell your cow.

Father distrusts this, however.   He only heard it about seven years ago, and I think he is a little doubtful of its good advice.

When a fine dry spring is followed by a wet hay-time, father always cheers us all up with:

> A dry May and a dripping June
> Brings all things in tune.

This was substantiated by one of the old farmers father knew in his youthful inexperienced days.   Father told him he had a lot of cut hay out in the meadows, and didn't know what to do with it; the old man looked at him.

'When you don't know what to do with hay, boy,' he said, 'let it alone, and another thing, boy, don't worry about spoiling a little hay.   You want to spoil some hay to have a good harvest.'

However, all these sayings are only the superficial trimmings of father's weather lore, and his knowledge of the weather is so much a part of him that it is almost a sixth sense. His distrust of an apparently fine morning so often turns out to be well founded. It is amazing to see his galvanic energy in infusing haste into a gang of haymakers, so that a field of hay is cocked before the storm, which only he suspects, arrives. Working leisurely, one is inclined to resent this pressing haste, but father has been home to look at the glass, and long before the black ominous clouds begin silently to mass on the horizon the whole gang is working at top speed without a word spoken. It is a very rare thing for father to be caught with a field of hay on the rake-row. Even last season, at the age of eighty, it took a good man to keep up with him at hay-cocking.

When we get a chilly day in early summer, and the men are working with their coats on, father says:

'It's the icebergs floating about in the Atlantic,' and as one works in the quiet fields the cold breeze brings a picture of a misty white ice mountain floating southward in far distant northern waters.

Old Mr. Pledger was always anxious during the early days of June. I can remember him meeting father one June morning, his face grave.

'Why, what's the matter with you this morning?' asked father.

'As soon as I put my foot outside the back door this morning I saw there'd been a white frost,' replied Mr. Pledger, 'and if you get a frost in June there won't be any corn.'

Sometimes, though, even with all these portents of disaster, we do get a good harvest, and my father never allows the weather to get him down. A few springs ago it rained solidly for two months, half our men went sick, and our lambs contracted a highly unpleasant disease of the joints, from which many died. Father took it all in his stride, and hardly raised his voice in complaint. The one thing that does annoy him is a tetchy seed-time, when the drill is for ever making false starts, and the men are wasting their time hooking and unhooking the horses. After this has happened once or twice father goes indoors and sits at his desk doing accounts; giving the weather time to improve and himself time to cool off.

If the weather looks like holding in a fine spell father takes a chance and, instead of rushing in straight away before the land is really dry, holds his hand till it dries out. Farming is almost as bad as racing. The farmer is gambling with the vagaries of the weather every day of his life.

A rather gushing lady visitor once greatly embarrassed me by asking if I wasn't my father's right hand. I hastened to assure her that this was not so.

'His right hand,' I said, 'is in the hall just inside the door. The weather glass.'

CHAPTER XV

STABLE STORIES

'Fust job I ever did they give me a bob a week. Seven year owd I was, and I used to goo pig tendin' in m' holidays from school. They used to run th' owd sows and pigs out on the fields, and I had to kip them from gooin' where they weren't suppose to.'

Old Ted seats himself more securely on the corn bin and watches his son, Young Ted (aged fifty-two), grooming his horses with a critical eye. Old Ted is getting on now, and can only do about a half day's work about the place on odd jobs, but there is nothing he likes better than to get into the stable of an evening when his son brings in his horses after their day's work. For Ted has been a horseman all his life, and the stable is his spiritual home. There he can sit and remember and talk about 'the owd days' to his son, or any one else who cares to listen.

The horses blow heavily and happily into their feed. The curry-comb scrapes roughly on a patch of dried sweat. A truss of sweet-smelling hay lies by the corn bin ready to fill up the hay racks.

Ted goes on:

'When I fust used to goo out in they fields I used to be a bit scairt,' he says. 'That was a tidy owd way from the farm, and I used to be scairt o' the quiet. Still, I got used to ut after a bit. Wust thing was they used to give me m' dinner in an owd bag, and they owd sows used to smell that. 'Course I warn't very big and I used to try and climb up a bit of a tree and hang that on one of the branches. They owd sows, though, they'd stand up on their hind legs against that tree and they could stand higher than I could climb. Many's the time I've lost m' dinner that way.'

Pausing for a moment he goes on:

'Once when that happened I was wonderful hungry, and there was some owd gipsies 'long o' their caravan up an owd grassy lane in they fields. They was a-cookin' suth'n' and that smelt beautiful! I walked across and looked at they. The smell was better than nuthin'.'

'"Will yer have some, boy?" they said.

'"Yes, I will," I said.

'That was all right. That was lovely. I enjoyed that.

'"Did yer like that, boy?" one o' the chaps asked me.

'"Yes, I did," I said. "Thank you."

'"What do reckon that was then, boy?" the same chap said again.

'"Rabbit," I said.

'Chap laughed. "No, boy," he say, "that were a nice young hedgehog."

'Now the last time I'd seen a hedgehog, that laid dead in a ditch just a-gooin' bad, and I thought o' that and I wondered whether they gipsies had got the one I'd been eatin' dead or alive. Lord, that made me feel bad. I think I was suthin' sick. I brought that owd hedgehog up all right. They gipsies laughed.

''Course,' said Ted, disparaging this former weakness, 'I weren't no age.'

Ted is in full spate now. He is back across the years to that small lonely figure in the fields.

'I used to goo bird scaring as well,' he remembers. 'Used to have an owd pair o' wooden clappers and used

kip walkin' round and round they owd fields all day shakin'
they and hollerin'. "Ha-ley, Ha-lay, Ha-lo!" we used to
shout. Lord, the time did go slow, though, sometimes that
seemed that never would be night. Sometimes, though, we
used to have a bit o' fun. I rec'lect once my eldest brother
was hoein' mangel in a field not far off where I was. So I
left the owd birds to have a bit of a feed, and I went across
to where he was and I crept up behind he. Then I shook
my clappers and hollered, and, my word, I think he jumped.
He turned round and swore at me.

'"Don't you never do that again, boy," he say. "You
want to fright anybody into the grave?"'

Young Ted has finished his horses now, and is standing
waiting to go home for his tea.

'Do you come home and have a cup o' tea, father,'
he says.

Old Ted slips slowly down off the corn bin. Always
the soul of hospitality, perhaps he will turn to where you
have been standing listening to him.

'Will yer have a cup o' tea long o' us?' he asks.

Gladly you accept, and are soon seated in the old cottage
kitchen with a cup of dark, richly brewed tea beside you.

Gently prompted, Ted returns to his youth.

'Did you ever have a gun of any kind to go bird scaring
with, Ted?'

Old Ted grins proudly.

'Yes, yes,' he says, 'I had an owd muzzle loader when I
got a bit owder. 'Course they only give me the powder
to make a noise with. They didn't give me ner shot.
First day I had it I bust the powder box a-jumpin' over a
gate. That made a tidy row, I think, but that didn't hurt
me. When I got used to it I used to load that up with
dried peas and little owd stones. Then I'd tie that on to a
gate-post with a bit o' rope, tie a bit o' string on to the
trigger, and then lay low till a few owd birds come down.

I allus used to be afraid that 'ud blow up, and I don't rec'lect that ever killed anything!

'That 's a good job my father never caught me at that,' Ted goes on. 'If he had done he 'd soon ha' given me a clout on the ear. Wonderful strict, my father was. There was nine of us children used to sit round the kitchen table at meal times. Father 'd only got to howd his hand up and you could ha' heard a pin drop. He was a big man, my father, with big hands. That made yer head ring when he gave yer one!'

He pauses to relight the 'Darkie' shag in his old clay pipe, and waits till it is drawing up before he speaks again.

'If we was at work with father and we got tired, none on us 'oon't let him see that. Once when father was chopping mangel out I was gooin' behind him a-singlin' of 'em. My back ached fit to break in two, and the tears ran down my face, but I kept my head down so he shouldn't see. I should ha' been 'shamed if he 'd seen me a-cryin'! 'Nother time I rec'lect was when I was a-drivin' the horse in the reaper.'

Suddenly Ted remembers that you probably don't know what the early reapers were like, though in his mind the implement is still as new and fresh and shining as the day it first came through the farmyard gate so many years ago.

'I don't suppose, though, you 've ever seen one o' them?' he asks rhetorically. 'No, no, that 'd be afore your time. Fust one we ever had, that wanted one to drive the horse and the other one sat on a seat on the platform. He had a rake, and as the corn fell on the platform he 'd rake that across. That took three sweeps with the rake to make a sheaf. Then he 'd shove that off the platform on to the ground to be tied up. Chaps 'ud be standing round the corn, each with his own stetch to keep tied up. When I was 'bout ten or eleven years owd they used to put me on the horse and father used to be on the seat. Sometimes father 'ud have a joke and 'stead of puttin' three sweeps

into one sheaf he 'd put six, so that made gret heavy owd
sheafs. Lord, that made they chaps swear. Father used
to laugh! I used to get so tired ridin' round and round
that field I 'd ha' given anything to get off th' owd horse
and have a rest, but that 'oon't do to tell father, so when I
got so I couldn't stick it no longer I used to shove m' owd
hat on one side of my head, and then I 'd stick my head up
and tilt it so the wind 'ud catch my hat and blow that off.
Then I had to stop th' owd horse and jump off and run and
fetch my hat. That give me a rest, and I could carry on
again. 'Course I couldn't do that often. Father 'd ha'
soon had suthin' to say.'

Ted talks on of how his father used to set rabbit snares
up on the field named 'Starve Larks,' and then send him
early next morning to go round the wires.

'Yer see father had to goo to work in the mornin' before
that was light in the winter, so I had to goo up Starve
Larks for they rabbits. They used to sit quiet in the
snares till I got up to 'em and then they 'd struggle and
scratch like mad, and they often used to get away. Tell
you the truth I was most as scairt of they rabbits as they
was o' me. I never told father 'bout the ones that got
away, but we lost a good few dinners, I can tell yer. Still
I didn't loose many once I got a year or two owder.'

'How old were you when you left school then, Ted?'
you ask as you rise to go. Young Ted's wife has gone
across to the cupboard, and has put a bottle of home-made
wine and three small glasses on the table, and old Ted
carefully fills the glasses before he answers.

'Seven years owd I was when I left school, and I went
straight from school into the harvest field 'long o' father.
He pitched and I was just man enough to load, but when
we got back to the stack I wasn't man enough to unpitch,
so father used to climb up on the wagon to do that. I used
to lay on the sheaves and have a rest. That was the best

part 'bout the job! Now then, do you have a glass o' Ted's wife's elderberry. You 'll find that drinks all right.'

And then out into the night with a warm glow of old elderberry. Out down the garden, and across the stack-yard, where the little boy lay comfortably on his loads in the September sunshine, while his father unpitched: up along the footpath that runs across Starve Larks, remembering a rabbit crouching in the grass stiff with fright as the small human comes to pick it up: the one last despairing effort against the cruelly tight wire, the small boy's nervous clumsiness, and then his tearful face watching his catch disappearing towards the distant hedge.

The next time you meet old Ted it is a cold winter's day, with grey sheets of rain driving across sodden countryside, and drumming on the stable roof. Ted is oiling the harness in the stable and, although it is early afternoon, he has a lantern lit to help him see his work. It throws a warm yellow light against the row of collars on their pegs, the hanging saddles and breechings, the trace harness, and the bridles. Among all the harness the light shows up a piece of white. There nailed on the wall is a printed schedule of the journeyings one season of a long forgotten stallion, Carslake Dalesman. It is faded now, and thick with dust and cobwebs. The horseman who nailed it there to remind himself of the Dalesman's arrival has long since gone his way. Only old Ted remembers the stallion's princely arrival one bright spring day, the mare's welcoming nicker from her stable, and the colt that he himself broke in some three years later. Straightening his back slowly he looks at the fading paper.

'Lovely colt, he was,' he says. 'We broke him in when he was just comin' three year owd. Lively young devil he was. We put a collar and trace harness on him first, and took him out in the front medder on a long rein. Round and round we had him, but that didn't make a mite o'

difference. Up to all manners o' tricks he was. The next
thing we did, we got a master gret owd log and put that
on the trace. 'Course we looked out for ourselves, you 're
sure! Then round and round and round again till we was
as sick of it as he was. Next day there was a wagon load
o' wheat goin' to Chelmsford, so we give him another
lesson. That was a double shaft wagon, so we put one
pair of good horses in the shafts, then the colt in trace
harness in front o' them, and then another good trace
horse in trace harness in front of him. So yer see he 'd
got to go. One in front on him pullin' and two behind
him pushin'. I don't reckon he enjoyed hisself much, but
he didn't behave hisself too badly, so on the way back we
put him and the front horse side by side in front of the
"fillers," [1] and drove the wagon home "four-in-hand."
We give him a lesson on the plough the followin' day. Half
a day three horses at length, one in front o' t'other, with
him the middle. Then, arter dinner, we left the front horse
in the stable, and put him in side by side with a good owd
horse which knowed his job. Oh, yes, he come to his
work all right. He come to his work!'

'Did you keep him here, Ted, or did he get sold?' you
ask curiously.

'Chap what had his mother kept him two or three year.
I disremember what happened to he in the finish. Captain they called he. Fine horse he grew to be.'

'Lot of horses get called Captain or Boxer, or some
such name, don't they, Ted?' you ask again.

Ted stops oiling the belly bands he's working on, and
lets his mind go back over his changes through the years.
He considers.

'I reckon you 're right,' he says at last. 'Moost o' the
horses I ever had have been Boxer, or Captain, or
Prince, or Short. They generally get called one o'

[1] Horses in shafts.

they four. I had a couple o' mares once, Darby and Tulip, and I've had a Ginger and a Bachelor. I had a wonderful awkward owd horse once called Dodman. He was the clumsiest animal ever drew breath, I should reckon. Our owd guv'nor allus has called anybody who's a bit awkward Dodman ever since. I reckon they use the same names so much 'cause they're simple, and th' owd horses can pick 'em up quick.'

Ted starts oiling again and, as he works, soliloquizes partly to himself, partly to you.

'Funny things, horses. You want to understand 'em. They're as different from one another as human bein's. Best owd horse ever I had was a grey. "Prince" they called he. Four or five year owd he was, and hadn't been broke long. Been broke rough too, he must ha' been. That had made he nervous. He didn't like strangers, but once he knowed yer he was like a child. Do anything you liked with him you could, but if anybody strange was a-workin' he, and they started to muck about and pull his reins and shout, he'd turn his head and look at they. "All right" he seemed to say, "two can play at that game." Then, whoever that was with he had got to look out. He'd show they a thing or two. Just the same he was if anybody strange was a-feedin' on him. He'd be as awkward as he could, stick his backside in the way, and sooner goo without his grub than take it from a stranger. They sowd he, come the finish. Said he was a "jib," 'oon't pull his loads, but he warn't no jib. That was just when he got it into his head that someone hadn't been treatin' he right. Poor old Prince, I missed he. Trouble was if I warn't here he 'oon't work rightly fer nobody else.'

Most of the harness is done now, but Ted finds one more pair of reins, and starts to work on them.

'Can't beat keepin' yer harness in good condition,' he says. 'I rec'lect one young chap used to work in this here stable 'long o' me, Bill Clasp his name was. Nice chap he was but he 'oon't take the trouble. Fond of his horses he was, too. He larnt his lesson though, that stayed with he all his life.'

'How did that happen then, Ted?' you ask.

'Well, that was like this. He was takin' a cart load of 'taters to the town one day and he 'd got a poor owd pair o' reins. Dry and brittle they were with a bit of a split in 'em. He ain't got far down the lane, narrer owd lane that was, ditches in both sides, when a car comes along like hell and all. 'Course Bill pulls in sharp to his near side, car just misses him, but his cart is down nearly in the ditch. He pulls sharp on his off rein, and that breaks like paper. That happens quick then. Cart wheel goos in the ditch. Over goos the whole lot. Horse on its side, layin' on a broken shaft, kickin' like blazes with fright, and tryin' to get up. Bill, he jumps clear as the cart goos over, and then comes back to sit on his horse's head to stop he from kickin' and hurtin' hisself. Then one of his mates turns up from somewhere and he sits on the horse's head while Bill tries to free the harness so the horse can get up. 'Course he can't work from behind the horse as he should 'cause that lays in the ditch and the hedge is in the way. So he has to work from the front. Then his mate, who 's a bit scairt, lets the horse get his head up. The horse kicks out fierce, and gets Bill right across the face, right from the middle o' the forehead, down his cheek, and round to his lips. He bled like a pig, but they got the horse's head down again, and he sat there and sent his mate for more help. We got there as quick as we could. One on us took Bill back to the farm, and the rest on us got the horse out. That warn't scratched, but Bill had that scar all his life. The mark of a horse shoe, right round his face.'

Ted finishes the reins and stands up, wiping his hands. After a bit he goes on talking again.

'Funny thing, every time I sit in this here owd stable

a-cleanin' harnesses I think of what happened to my poor owd missus.'

'What was that then, Ted?' you ask again. The story will not be told unless a keen and appreciative interest is actively shown.

'I was sittin' here oiling harness, same as I am to-day, and my missus she wanted me for suthin'. She thought I was in the barn mendin' sacks, so she took a short cut across the cow yard. There was only one owd cow stood there, with its calf, the guv'nor had bought that the day before at market. That didn't take a mite o' notice o' the missus as she went across to the barn. 'Course she found out I weren't there, and turned round to come back. She hadn't got half way back across the yard when that cow ran at she like lightnin'. God knows what happened. I reckon the missus had her mouth open to shout at it. Anyway, that got one of its horns right inside her mouth, so that come out half way up the side of her nose, then that pulled its head back, and opened her face from there down to her lips. She got away then, and ran back to the cottage. She didn't know what had happened till she looked in the glass. She hadn't felt nuthin', yer see. When she saw her face she went upstairs and got a clean sheet. Then she held that over her face, and came to look for me again. I shan't never forget that. "What ever's the matter with you, gal?" I says. She took down the sheet, that was smothered in blood, then I looked at her face. As I say, I shan't never forget that. I harnessed the guv'nor's owd cob and trap quickest I ever did in my life, and drove th' owd cob ter Chelmsford as quick as he'd ever been there. Her face got poisoned, and she was took very queer for a long time, but she got over it in the finish. Didn't show a lot neither. Still, I shan't never forget it.'

The first team of horses are coming into the stable now. Suffolks they are, and they've been to the mill with a wagon load of wheat. Old Ted speaks to them as they pass him, and they prick up their ears. Young Ted has a team of Shires in another wagon, which will be in in a few minutes. His father keeps gazing out of the door and down the road, to see if he is coming. As he watches the road he talks of Suffolks and Shires, of how a man's taste in the teams he drives may vary.

'Owd Arthur Thompson was my mate when I first took on horseman here. He'd just come from another farm. He'd had a team of three Shires for nine or ten year. Broke 'em all hisself he had, and he loved they like children. He could do anything with 'em, and they'd do anything for he. They was pretty to watch together. That farm bordered on ourn, and we often used to see owd Arthur with his team. Then his guv'nor bought some more farms, and took a fancy to Suffolk horses. All his farms had got to have Suffolks. So he sowd owd Arthur's team, and give he three six-year-owd Suffolks. That broke the owd man's heart. If they'd ha' give he the Suffolks young, so he could ha' broken 'em to his own ways, that might ha' been all right, but they were six year owd, and set in their ways. He tried for a year, but that weren't no good, and he give in his notice. His guv'nor was sorry to see him goo, and he asked why he was a-gooin'. "You hadn't ought to ha' sowd all my horses, master," owd Arthur said. "That 'ould ha' been all right if I'd been a younger man. I reckon you can't teach an owd dog new tricks." He didn't stop long at our place neither, the horses were Shires, but they weren't his Shires. I rec'lect he went on the road come the finish.'

Young Ted's wagon is in sight now, and his father gets busy over the corn bin with the feed for the horses. The wagon turns off the road and rattles noisily into the yard. The horses stamp and shake their heads. Another day is over. Another journey done!

CHAPTFR XVI

FARM HUMOUR

'WHY, look at they come out to look at us!' exclaimed
Jim Coe, excitedly turning round to the rest of his party
seated on the upper deck of a bus on its way through the
city. The West Hanningfield choir was on its annual
outing, its destination the zoo. What had so gratified
Jim in the interest taken was the crowds of city workers
pouring out for their lunch.

For lunch that day the party had had fruit and junket
for the second course, and Tom Thrush, who had never
eaten junket before, had quite a shock. It was a thick
well-set junket, and Tom took a spoonful and bit it hard.
His teeth fairly rattled, and everybody stopped eating to
look at him.

'Well,' Tom said slowly, 'I don't think much of that
stuff. There ain't no body to it!'

Such outings as these and the anecdotes they provided
would cause many a hearty laugh next harvest time, each
story repeated slowly at least three or four times, so that
every possible dreg of humour might be strained from it,
and enjoyed to the full. Most farms have their wit, who
keeps the gang laughing at hay-time and harvest, telling

tales of holidays, peculiarities of neighbours in ways or speech, or humorous happenings in the day's work.

Sitting on the side of his wagon, his load unpitched, he waits for the horseman to lead away for the next load. Meanwhile he grins up at the stacker.

'Did you hear 'bout Jim Mann's girl what goos to work up the rectory. Well, she takes a wonderful pride in whitenin' that front door step, and they swallers make a terrible mess on that every day. They rile that girl proper. Well, th' other day she saw parson's wife a pepperin' a corner o' the dinin'-room, where their young kitten had done as it shouldn't. What must she do then next mornin' but goo out and pepper that front step 'gainst they swallers!'

As the wagon rolls away he stands in the back, leaning on his fork, shaken with laughter. On his return it is to talk of old Fred, who always calls nightingales 'them noise-buds,' or to mention old Sally Carey down the village, who said she reckoned 'stronomy' was a wonderful thing, but what beat her was how they found out the names of the stars.

At tea time, when the women come walking up the stubble carrying their husbands' straw tea baskets, they may be talking of old Charlie the cowman. Stretched in the shade, their backs against the stack, they recall his escapades.

'Do you rec'lect the night owd Charlie had so much home-made wine he couldn't remember whether he got to goo home or goo to work? So he split the difference and went up the farm and laid down between a couple o' the cows. Next mornin' he said he didn't know any difference 'tween bein' there or in bed with his missus.'

Someone else caps this quickly. 'Owd Charlie allus says that when he was courtin' and he and his missus went for a walk, they was allus a-bumpin' into one another. Now he says one walks one side o' the road and one walks t'other, and then the road ain't big enough.'

Tea is nearly finished now, and the men get up slowly, one by one, and stroll across to the gate for a smoke away from the stacks. They are still laughing about Charlie: about his habit of voluble and lengthy swearing to himself when things go wrong. For Charlie is nearly stone deaf now, and as he can't hear himself swearing he reckons no one else can either. Several incidents are remembered with pleasure, and his latest flow recounted with full flavour.

'I was in the cart lodge t' other day and owd Charlie didn't see me. He was harnessing the pony up, and the back chain broke, and let the shafts down on his feet. Lord, you should 've heard him carry on. That was a fair treat. He said——,' and the speaker gives Charlie's comments in detail.

The laughter rocks round the gate as the horsemen go to take the nosebags off and get the wagons running again.

'Time they wheels were a-turnin' again,' they say.

Syd Bright, a horseman, was a tall man with a very short wife. The night before he was married they had the piano going down in the pub. Everybody was buying Syd pints and, about a quarter to ten, when he was standing at the bar with a half-full pint pot in one hand and a full one in the other, someone struck up:

'Isn't it a pity that the likes of her should put upon the likes of him?'

Syd joined in with the best, swinging his pint pots to the music, and as proud of his short bride to be as any man could be.

Syd's wife's shortness became a legend which Syd himself did his best to foster, and even improve on. There was one memorable occasion when he was taking his horses back to the farm after a day's work. He was stopped by a stranger on a bicycle who asked for Mrs. Bright's cottage, explaining that he was the new insurance man, and had come to collect the weekly due.

'Recken I can,' said Syd slowly, ''means she's my missus, but that ain't ner good you a-gooin' there 'cause she ain't at home. She's gone down the village 'long o' my youngest. Wonderful short, she is, my missus. She ought to be on her way home by now. Do you keep on stret down this road, and if you see a pram comin' towards yer with nothin' behind it, you'll know that's my missus.'

It was Syd who was the kindly guardian of his dim-witted and much chaffed mate, Bert—Bert, who was generally known as 'Rusty and Bright,' in memory of the time when he was told to grease his cart and, when asked the state of the axles, replied:

'They ain't too bad. Rusty and bright they are.' On a pouring wet day he would come into the barn shaking the water from his coat. 'That's wet and it rains' he would observe sagely.

Occasionally Syd could be persuaded to tell of the many eccentricities of a farmer whom he had once worked for. Of how, late in life, his employer laboured under the impression that everybody was out to 'do' him. One of the strange results of this was when the farmer, who had bought a new horn for his car, carried it about with him all day on the farm. He was not sure if it was quite what he wanted, or really reliable, and all day startled animals and workers would jump suddenly to a nearby HONK, as he pressed the bulb, listening intently, his head on one side.

Another time he bought a raincoat in the early summer. Weeks of fine dry weather turned into months, and still he had no chance to try it out. At length his patience was exhausted. He had to find out if the coat was worth the money he had paid for it. His startled workers were met by a strange sight next morning when they arrived for the day's work. The coat was draped over the clothes line in the backyard, and the old gentleman was busily engaged throwing buckets of water at it to see if it kept the wet out.

One old Essex parson loved to repeat some of the homely versions of the church service prayers as revised by one of his choirmen, Arthur Rawling, a stockman. For instance, there was the simply expressed confession:

'What we left undone be done, but what we hadn't ought to ha' done be undone.'

At a choirmen's meeting one night the subject of Arthur's prayers was brought up by a fellow choirman.

'Have you heard what he say in the Litany, parson?'

'No,' said parson, 'I can't say I have.'

'Well, he say: "have mussy upon us missable fenders," but he don't say nawthin' 'bout they other fire-irons.'

The same Arthur Rawling was somewhat bothered on one occasion when a fête was held in the parsonage garden in aid of a missionary society. The principal exhibit was a model Zulu kraal. Arthur was worried by the word 'kraal.' He inspected the small beehive-like huts with their low openings carefully, and then decided what he wanted was a pint. On his way down the parsonage drive he ran into a newly arrived acquaintance, who inquired of him: 'What's this here Zulu kraal?'

'I don't rightly know, mate,' Arthur replied slowly, 'but what I reckon is they call it that 'cause these here black chaps have to crawl into 'em.'

Nearly all the old hands at Link House had their nick-names, and were seldom known by anything else. There was 'Farmer' Tyler, so called because he took, if possible, even more interest in the working of the land and running of the farm than father himself. 'Butty' Cox was less easy to explain, but had certain implications. 'Squeaker' Argent was so called because his voice broke into a high shrill note of annoyance when his horses did something that didn't suit him. 'Bryant' May was obvious.

'Here comes "Farmer," the men would say, as they stood on some job waiting for orders. 'He 'll know what to do as well as the guv'nor.' And he did.

There was one small farmer whose land adjoined Link House who was really notorious for his steady, unremitting, slogging hard work. He even deeply impressed father, who is not much of a one for standing about himself.

He was a north-country man named Downes, and on one occasion father asked him if he ever took a pint of beer to ease his endless toil.

Mr. Downes looked hard at father. 'No,' he said, 'I never touch anything but water. There 's a lot of goodness in water, Mr. Smith.'

'I believe you,' said father.

'Have you ever tried it for working on, Mr. Smith?' pursued Mr. Downes.

'No,' replied father, hurriedly terminating a conversation which held such an unpleasant prospect, 'and I don't intend.'

In the old days a man who came into a village from another district, probably not many miles distant, would be regarded as a 'furriner,' and be looked on with some suspicion until people got to know him, or somebody local vouched for him as 'all right.'

In one little village in north Essex the rector had retired to bed early one summer Sunday night. Outside his rectory was the little village green with its duck-pond, and this evening there was a noisy group round the pond who prevented the rector from slipping off to sleep as early as he might have done. The village lads had had a pint or two before the pub shut, and now were loath to go home to bed. The conversation grew louder and louder, voices were raised in angry argument.

The rector turned uneasily in his bed, wondering if it was his duty to go and put a stop to this riot. Suddenly it was decided for him. There was a shout, a loud splash, roars of laughter, and then silence settled deeply on the village.

Directly after breakfast the following morning the rector sought out his gardener's boy, one Sammy Cartwright. 'A lively lad' they called him in the village.

'Well Sammy,' asked the rector, 'what were you up to last night on the green? I very nearly came out after you. There wasn't a soul in the place could get a wink of sleep with your infernal racket.'

'Well, sir,' said Sammy, 'we 're sorry there were so much row, but that weren't our fault. No, that that weren't.'

'Whose fault was it then?' inquired the rector irritably.

'That were an owd furriner,' Sammy replied vehemently. 'We was a-talkin' afore we went home, and he come across the green to us. Come from th' other side o' Chelmsford (pronounced Chelmsud) he did. Started askin' questions 'bout one thing and another. We didn't like that. Come to the finish I said to he, I said: "What business might that be o' yourn then?" He was leanin' 'gainst the pond fence, and he answered a bit cheeky like, so I said no more. I shoved he head over tip into the pond. He come out there a-dreenin' a' slud. I don't reckon he 'll come here ner more.'

'No,' said the rector, as he turned away, 'I don't suppose he will.'

It was at this same rector's church that four old retired farm workers never missed a service. Always at least a quarter of an hour early they would stand outside the porch in their smocks and beaver hats waiting till all the 'quality' had gone in. Then, always led by one of their number named Charlie Sawyer, they made their solemn entry, breathed some preliminary words into their beaver hats, and sat back, ready both to appreciate and criticize the service and the rector's sermon.

Old Charlie Sawyer was a great character, one of whose

chief claims to fame was the magnificent rhubarb he grew in his cottage garden. 'Ivory Cottage' he called his home, because of the ivy that climbed all over it.

Leaning on his garden gate smoking on a summer evening, he was gratified when one of the younger men, on his way home perhaps from the hayfield, stopped for a chat with him. After talking over the day's work it was usual to admire old Charlie's rhubarb. There it stood with sturdy stalks and enormous leaves like a grove of young palm-trees.

Charlie would turn and regard his pride with a grudging eye.

'Yes,' he 'd say. 'They 're master gret owd rhubarb. Th' owd general up at the Court give me they roots. They do well in this owd garden.'

Then would follow his famous rhubarb story.

'I rec'let one night that was a-rainin', and I was in bed 'long of my missus. Half asleep I was, when she nudged me in the ribs.

'"Charlie," she say, "there's a noise downstairs. I reckon that's someone a-bugglin."

'"Don't be so silly," I say. "We ain't got nothin' wuth bugglin'."

'Still, come to the finish she 'oon't lay still, kept on about there was a noise, and that was a buggler, and I could hear that too.

'So I got out of bed and went to the winder, frorn o' cowd I was, and do you know what that noise was? That was they rain drops a-rottlin' down on they gret owd rhubarb leaves.'

But always the chief source of farm humour is the ordinary everyday happenings at work, and the continual leg-pulling that goes on between the farm workers. Most of them masters of all their many trades, it is their delight to seize upon their mates' occasional shortcomings.

F

Perhaps it may be a stack leaning drunkenly after harvest, supported by three or four stout pieces of wood.

'We 'll tell owd George 'bout that,' they say, mentioning the stacker.　Then meeting George:

'I see that owd stack o' yourn wants some "legs" then.'

George grins sheepishly, but always the joke is appreciated as much by the victim as by the leg-puller, and is given and taken in friendship and good humour.

CHAPTER XVII

BETWEEN WARS

JOHN BUCHAN, in his autobiography, *Memory Hold-the-Door*, made the interesting statement that 'As one ages, the memory seems to be inverted, and recent events to grow dim in the same proportion as ancient happenings become clear.'

This describes better than I could attempt to do what has happened to my father's memory with regard to the twenty years' interval between the last and this present war. He attacks the everyday farming problems with the same verve and vigour, however, and rarely sighs for the 'good old days.'

In view of this, and the fact that the story of the plight of agriculture between 1918 and 1939 makes but sorry reading in any case, I will pass over these years quickly. They were years when the humorous remark that farmers 'live on their losses' became for many of them a dangerously grim reality.

The years 1919 and 1920 saw prices well maintained and, in some cases, reaching higher levels. Implements at farm sales made fantastic prices. Agriculture was all set for a golden age.

Then in 1921 came the first grumblings of the depression with which the world had to grapple as an aftermath of the war. Prices began to fall, and farmers who had 'eaten and drunk and been merry' began to feel the first chill winds of changing times. However, the harvest that year was exceptionally good, almost of the 1911 vintage, and the bad times that lay ahead could not be visualized even by the most far-seeing farmer.

This same year we were obliged to leave Link House, as our lease had expired, and the landlord now demanded a rent increased to an impossible amount. It must have been a great wrench for father to make the decision to leave. There had been Smiths at Link House for a hundred and thirty years, and mine was the fifth generation to be born in the farmhouse.

Mother and father now started what seemed an endless series of peregrinations to view various farms, and mother had many doubtful moments when she thought father was on the point of taking one or another where she did not care for the house. Mother had a great ambition, that the new farm should have the actual farmhouse some distance from the buildings. Any one who has lived close to farm buildings in hot weather will appreciate why. One hot summer afternoon she remembers vividly. She and father had driven over to a farm in one of the really ugly flat areas of Essex, where the land was extremely good, and father greatly fancied the quality of the crops they passed on the road. On arrival at the farmhouse father started off on a tour round the farm, and mother was left with the farmer's wife to inspect the house and garden. The house was square and ugly, and abutted on the cow shed and

Evening Walk

the bullock yard.   After a thorough tour, in which mother was a most unenthusiastic sightseer, they went into the dining-room for tea.   Every plate on the table was covered with a gauze frame.   Above them hovered a thin cloud of flies.   From the ceiling, moving sluggishly in the breeze, hung three fly-papers.   The farmer's wife caught mother's gaze.

'Yes,' she said, 'I'm afraid we do get a few flies.'

Father came in soon after, very enthusiastic about the land and crops, and mother's heart sank.   To complete her misery, the door of the cow shed opened, outside the window.   Milking was over, and the cows began to file out on their way to the meadows.   It was now obvious that the flies which hovered over the table were merely a covering force, while the main army concentrated on the cow shed.   As each cow passed the window its attendant flies deserted it *en masse*, and joined the besiegers about the cake plates.   The fly-papers took but an imperceptible toll.

I don't know what was said on the journey home, but it was funny how quickly father's enthusiasm waned.   It wasn't quite the place he wanted after all.

The good offices of Mr. Silas Pledger of Old Lodge, Springfield, eventually brought the search to a close.   He put father in touch with Mr. Herbert Gray (of Gray's Brewery in Chelmsford), who was reducing his farming activities, and from him father bought Belstead Hall and Hill Farm, consisting of some two hundred odd acres, in the parish of Broomfield, and about three miles to the north-east of Chelmsford, with possession at Michaelmas 1921. The farms had three good double-tenement cottages, but no farmhouse, and so, after considering altering one of the cottages, father decided to build, and mother selected a pleasant site on the gentle slope overlooking the Chelmer valley.   It was some two hundred yards from the farm buildings.

The Link House sale of live and dead stock was held in the front meadow, while the furniture, much of which mother disposed of, was sold in the old cobbled back yard. Mother had a large lunch for buyers in the old tub house, where father had conducted his brewing operations so many years before, and a good time was had by all. It was certainly a good sale, and father was thoroughly satisfied. And so, a few days later, father drove away from the old house, away from the tall poplars in the orchard, away from the old magnolia, and away down the lane past the chestnut-trees.

When, after two or three years, Link House and its attendant farms fell into neglect and waste, father always avoided going back there on our occasional visits to West Hanningfield. It hurt him to see the fields derelict and hedges high and overgrown, but most of all it hurt him to think of the old house falling slowly and quietly into disrepair. Some fourteen years after we left West Hanningfield we induced him to drive us over to Cannon Barns one lovely Sunday evening in May. Mother wanted some bluebells, and there were always bluebells in Handle Grove, behind Cannon Barns. There was just room for the car between the hedges, and when we reached Cannon Barns, always an isolated farm, the silence was almost oppressive. The big Dutch barn and buildings which father had built after the fire still stood in good repair, but cattle had been in the house, and the roof had fallen in.

'Let's walk across to Hophedges,' father said.

The rabbits scattered endlessly in front of us. The hedges and brambles were stretching out into the fields. The cuckoo's call came ceaselessly. The desolation was eerie in the summer sunlight. We crested a rise in the ground.

'There's Partridge's,' said father.

The nettles were growing thickly round the bullock-yard posts. The cottage chimney-stack stood gaunt against an old plum-tree.

'I remember . . .' father said, and then fell silent. There must have been too much he remembered.

These farms were but a small proportion of a vast area of land in that district which fell out of cultivation, and only began to be brought back under the plough a year or so before the present war. It must never be allowed to happen again.

As our house could not be finished for some time, we went first to live at the Red House at Great Waltham, some three miles away from our new farms. From here father either drove or cycled to work. It will be realized that the work entailed in giving up farms and taking over new land is very considerable. Valuations, sales, and the general shift-over, meetings with lawyers, auctioneers, etc., entail a vast amount of extra work, and when, on top of this, father had a three-mile journey night and morning, instead of going straight out of his back door into the farmyard, he found it pretty heavy going and, for about the first time, admitted it. The doctors feared that he had serious heart trouble, and there was talk of beds downstairs and taking things easy. Father picked up again, but was still not quite himself, and mother watched him anxiously. What he really needed was a good rest and holiday, but this would have been such purgatory to him that it would have done him more harm than good.

From the Red House we moved to a small house in Broomfield, and then, finally, in December 1922, into our newly completed Hill House. Father sat by the hall fireside the first night and stretched his legs comfortably to the blaze.

'It's good to sit under your own roof again,' he said with deep relish. The gipsy life of three moves in the last eleven months had left him more firmly convinced than ever that a man's home is his castle, and that there's no bed like your own bed.

J K Popham

Buildings at Hill Farm, Broomfield

The 1922 harvest in the new farms was good, averaging over six quarters per acre, and father was well satisfied, but on 12th November he came home from Chelmsford Fair feeling ill, and never went outdoors again till Boxing Day. The doctors once more diagnosed heart trouble, and it almost seemed that father might become a permanent invalid. His bed must be put in the dining-room. He must on no account walk upstairs. Then, on Boxing Day, the late Dr. Smallwood, of Great Waltham, came to see father with a view to hiring the shooting over the farms for the next season. Mother had been anxious for another opinion for some time, and she now asked him to examine father, and give his view.

'He 's all right,' said Dr. Smallwood. 'He 's been over-doing it, and a good rest has done him good. Most of the rest of the trouble is indigestion. He 's good for another twenty years.'

'Can I go out, sir?' was father's anxious inquiry, and away he went across to the farm; and that was twenty years ago.

Only two of the old Link House men moved with us to Broomfield, Bill Snell and Harry Cox, Bill to Belstead Hall, and Harry to Hill Farm. In the rest of the cottages Mr. Gray's men stayed on with us. In 1924, however, we were joined by yet another of father's old West Hanning-field stalwarts. Adjoining our southern boundary in the parish of Springfield lay Nabbotts Farm, of something under two hundred acres, and farmed by Mr. Adolphus Pledger, the brother of Silas. The land lay conveniently in with ours, and I think that father had often cast covetous glances at it, so that when Mr. Adolphus came to him one day in the summer of 1924 and said that he was giving up the lease, and would father care to take over the farm, father was overjoyed. He accompanied Mr. Adolphus to London to see Mr. Kitchin, the landlord, everything worked out satisfactorily and, after the usual formalities, father took over Nabbotts. Hearing that father would be wanting another man or two, Alfred Tyler came to see him, and father soon set him on, for Alfred was one of the last of that fast vanishing race, the master ploughman, carpenter, stacker, hedger, or almost anything he liked to lay his hand to.

Mr. Kitchin, the Nabbotts landlord, was a great personality. A wealthy landowner, and a director of the London and North Eastern Railway, he lived near Darlington, and only came down to London twice a year. On these occasions father was summoned to the presence to pay the rent, and always returned with tales of titanic arguments on the type of paint to be used for painting repairs, or some such thing.

'White paint, Smith, with a good lead base, is the only paint.'

When father pointed out that white isn't really a practicable colour for the outside of farm buildings, he was heavily overruled, and white it had to be. To my deep regret I was sent away on the occasion of his only visit to us, when he stayed one night. He had an extremely unruly set of false teeth, and father felt they might be too much for me.

When he died a few years ago father was given the first offer of the farm, and took it over. I think he misses his visits to Mr. Kitchin's house at Richmond, with the study lined with pictures of 'Puffing Billy,' and the lengthy arguments and cups of strong coffee. He always seemed to come home stimulated.

No account of my father's life would be complete without some description of the man who was undoubtedly his best friend, Mr. Silas Pledger. His farm, Old Lodge, bordered our eastern boundary, and as he could do no active work himself, he often strolled down the lovely avenue of elms,

which ran from his pleasant grey-brick farmhouse to the
road, in search of my father and talk. There was nothing
father enjoyed more than a good farming talk with Mr.
Pledger, but there were occasions when time was short
and work was pressing.

Mr. Pledger, outside Old Lodge gates, would see father's
distant figure approaching down Belstead Hall lane on a
bicycle, and as soon as the bike reached hailing distance
would let out a roaring stentorian bellow: 'JOHN! JOHN!'

On normal days father would turn his bike at the end of
the lane and cycle up to the lodge gates to enjoy a pleasant
half hour's chat, but on the other busy days his bike would
continue inexorably on its way, while the countryside
echoed and re-echoed with a crescendo of 'JOHNS!'

Father's obvious ignoring of these calls was often brought
up at their next meeting, but father always professed hard
hearing or a contrary wind, and I suppose Mr. Pledger
understood anyway.

For Mr. Pledger was stout and getting on in years, and a
rapid pursuit was out of the question. However, it was
surprising the distances he covered by gentle and easy
stages. We live about a mile and a half by road from
Old Lodge, but many were the Sunday evenings when a
rousing knock on the front door would proclaim Mr.
Pledger's arrival. He would stay for a couple of hours
talking to father of every agricultural matter under sun and
storm, of which he had great wise and working knowledge.
Then he would get up to go. If it was a dark night father
would offer to accompany him till his eyes grew used to the
darkness. This offer was always indignantly refused. With
a chorus of 'good nights' Mr. Pledger would edge off from
the front doorstep like a ship leaving harbour cautiously in
a thick fog. His footsteps would recede, and then come
nearer, again and again. Father would stand motionless
in the doorway, waiting. At last the appeal: ' John, John,

I can't find my way out of the gate!' Father would immediately disappear into the night, guide Mr. Pledger through
the gate, and then the two friends would walk away up the
road, immersed again in talk. Father would reappear half
an hour or so later, having walked maybe half the way
to Old Lodge.

Our garden, like those of most farmers, begins to look a
bit down at heel in the late summer and early autumn. The
men are all out in the fields, and so the lawns remain uncut,
the edges grow ragged, and all the farmers' wives' efforts
cannot keep up with the deterioration. One year when
our garden was in a more than usually acute state of disrepair, Mr. Pledger drove by in his dog-cart. Seeing
father at his desk in the hall, he pulled up. Father opened
the window and leaned out.

'They say a bad gardener makes a good farmer, don't
they, John?' he shouted, then whipped up his horse and
was gone down the road. After lunch father found things
were a bit slack anyway, and sent a man to get the lawns cut.

In the autumn of 1930 I came home from school and,
after six months at an agricultural college, joined father on
the farm. I was very full of information and very willing
to show everybody how to do everything. My particular
line, I thought, was hens. I wanted to take over all the
farm poultry, modernize, mechanize, and generally make it
go. Father was sceptical, but willing to give me a certain
amount of rope. For three years I cleaned out chicken
houses, washed eggs, reared chicks, fought the ever-
prevalent and insidious diseases, and then the infinitely
superior delights of general farming dawned on me. Father
had kept a flock of eighty to a hundred half-bred breeding
ewes since 1924, and to these and the hundred and one
other branches of general farming I was eventually drawn.
Poultry had broken my spirit, as it has many another's, and
I came to my new job a very humble young man.

My father has been the best tutor in the world, and if the times were unfortunate for a young man starting, they were no worse for him than for those who have known the better days. It is well to remember the saying: 'Farming is not a way of making a living, but a mode of life.'

A great deal has been written on the subject of the farming depression in the years between the wars, and many sorry tales have been told. To these I wish to contribute nothing, wishing only to present briefly my father's memories of his farming life, and give some picture of the old peaceful days and farming ways. Father is eighty-one next birthday, as lively and upright as ever, bicycles everywhere, works a full eight hours a day, and is most receptive to modern ideas. Sometimes he disappears for two or three hours, and we hope that perhaps he is taking a well-earned rest. However, he always reappears steadily pedalling along the lanes, having gone perhaps to Chelmsford for a machine part, or to Hatfield Peverel to see the wheelwright, or to Little Waltham to the harness maker. The average person when asked to guess his age puts him at sixty to sixty-five.

His recipe? 'We brewed our own good beer, and we lived straight and hard when we were young, boy!' And they did.

EPILOGUE

CONVERSATION WITH A SENTRY

FATHER straightened his back slowly and regarded the two rather spindly lambs, now busy obtaining their first meal on earth, with a disparaging gaze.

'Leggy little devils,' he said. He always says this every year about most of his lambs, as if he expected them all to die at any moment.

The sheep are lambing down on the horse meadow this year. Three acres of this are fenced off on one side of the meadow for a searchlight site, and the ewe father was now watching had lambed down close to this fence.

The sentry on duty, his rifle slung over his shoulder, was standing on the other side of the fence watching with rapt attention as the lambs filled themselves. He had been born and bred in a north London suburb, and had never spent more than a day or two in the country before in his life.

It should be explained here that a sentry in a searchlight site has a roving commission centring round the Lewis gun emplacement. He carries binoculars and a whistle, which he sounds when anything approaches the site. Needless to say, there are times in a three-hour watch when things are a little slack.

The ewe and her family being safely settled, father was in a conversational mood, and soon he and the sentry were deep in talk—the sentry with a weather eye open in case an army lorry or officer's car arrived.

The talk drifted back to the last war. Father spoke of German prisoners that had worked for him, and the sentry discovered that father had been to school in his suburb. The farmer and the soldier were delighted to discuss this common bond, and a large army lorry was nearly in the horse meadow before the sentry spotted it and blew his whistle.

The lambs had finished their feed and lay down. Their mother began to graze a few feet away.

A light wind sprang up, and the sentry looked up at the sky.

'Is it going to rain, sir?' he asked.

Father glanced up before he replied:

'No, boy. There's no rain in those clouds.'